TUGS & TOWING

Patrick Stephens Limited, a member of the Haynes Publishing Group, has published authoritative, quality books for enthusiasts for more than twenty years. During that time the company has established a reputation as one of the world's leading publishers of books on aviation, maritime, military, model-making, motor cycling, motoring, motor racing, railway and railway modelling subjects. Readers or authors with suggestions for books they would like to see published are invited to write to: The Editorial Director, Patrick Stephens Limited, Sparkford, Nr Yeovil, Somerset BA22 7JJ.

TUGS & TOWING

A worldwide survey of the vessels, techniques and development of the towage business

M J GASTON

Foreword by Anthony Knight

PSL

Patrick Stephens Limited

First published 1991

© M. J. Gaston 1991

British Library Cataloguing in Publication Data

Gaston, M. J.
Tugs and towing.
1. Tugs, history
I. Title
623.823209

ISBN 1-85260-252-X

Patrick Stephens Limited is a member of the Haynes Publishing
Group P.L.C., Sparkford, Nr Yeovil, Somerset BA22 7JJ.

Typeset by FWT Studios Limited, Wellingborough, Northants

Printed in Great Britain

1 3 5 7 9 10 8 6 4 2

Contents

Acknowledgements

I would like to thank the very many towage companies, their employees, and my many friends in the industry for their enormous support and encouragement. They have all shown great patience in answering my endless questions and allowing me access to their vessels. Special thanks are due to the staff at various branches of the Alexandra Towing Company Ltd, J. P. Knight Ltd, and Cory Towage Ltd.

My sincere thanks are also due to Ray Anderson and David Brown for their painstaking scrutiny of the draft manuscript. I am also indebted to Lawrence Amboldt and all the other photographers and companies who so readily allowed me to use their pictures, which are credited appropriately in the captions. The line illustrations would not have been possible without the help of Dave Lane and his friends who translated my strange sketches into presentable artwork.

Finally, my grateful thanks are due to my wife Ann and the rest of the family who have endured even longer periods of absence than usual, whilst the final manuscript was being prepared.

M.J.G.

Foreword
by Anthony Knight
Member of the Executive Committee of the
British Tugowners Association

Who better than Jack Gaston to write this book? Well known, widely respected and engaged in the towing industry for many years, yet not within its thirlage, Mr Gaston has amassed a knowledge that is free from the prejudice possessed by most professional tugmen. Much to the advantage of the book and to the credit of its author, its content is fact and not opinion.

'Tugs' and 'Towing' are two separate subjects. A tug is the finished product of an engineering exercise that matches propulsion units to a hull, whilst towing is a discipline concerned with seamanship and ship handling (yes, tugs are ships!). There have been published many books that deal with either the one subject or the other, but this is the first serious attempt at bringing together, under one cover, the many elements that compose our industry. As such its appeal will be widespread. To the amateur it will instruct and amuse: to the professional it will remind. But most of all it gives to those of us to whom the future of towage is entrusted a tool for the induction of new entrants.

The author in writing and the publisher in producing a book not confined to technicalities have also performed another service much needed by the industry. They offer an attractive package, agreeable to read, to an audience more catholic than just tug lovers. The casual readers, of whom there will be many, will become aware of the versatility of the modern tug and its importance to the marine world. Aware, too, of the many different qualities required by our tugmen for the adequate discharge of their duties, often under conditions of hardship. An end, in short, to the unfair if endearing image of 'Tugboat Annie'.

This well-illustrated book merits a generous reception and it will, I hope, be up-dated from time to time.

Introduction

The tug has developed steadily over the last century and a half, hand in hand with progress made in the parent shipping industry, into a highly specialized and sometimes complex vessel. The present day towage scene, both in harbour and at sea, is one that reflects continually changing technology, coupled with an air of maturity resulting from many decades of evolution.

The main purpose of this book is to describe and illustrate the many facets of what has become a highly sophisticated industry and its vessels. The intention has been to tackle the subject in terms simple enough for the uninitiated, yet with sufficient detail to interest the tugman. A brief historical section has been added in order to illustrate the way that tugs and towage have developed and to put into perspective the particularly rapid progress made in the last few decades. No attempt has been made to record anything approaching a complete history of the 150 years of tug operation. Such a work would run into several volumes.

Considerable thought went into deciding how the space available would be used. Towage is a world-wide activity and tugs range from very small workboats towing logs on remote rivers to powerful deep sea vessels towing ships and huge inanimate objects across the world's oceans. Although the contents have a strong British and European flavour an earnest attempt has been made to cover most of the principal types of tugs and their uses, wherever they may be employed. An exception is the oil rig supply vessel. I readily acknowledge that this type of ship frequently has a significant towing capability. But the primary role of such a vessel is to provide a whole range of specialist services, of which towage may be only a part, and for this reason they are not covered in any detail.

Following the historical section are chapters dealing with modern tug propulsion systems, towing gear, and ancillary equipment. Tug owners now have available a greater choice of technology and alternative systems than ever before. The most important propulsion systems and their principles of operation are illustrated, along with the bewildering variety of controls. A similar approach has been taken with towing gear, which may perhaps be regarded as the second most important feature of the tug.'Ancillary equipment' is the title chosen to cover much of the other marine equipment, concentrating on those items which are particularly important aboard a tug. Subsequent chapters deal with the various types of tug and illustrate, in rather more specific terms, how the propulsion systems and equipment are employed.

Full technical specifications for every vessel mentioned and their individual histories have not been possible due to space limitations. The information provided is intended to highlight specific points and enable sensible comparisons to be made. Year of construction, gross registered tonnage, overall length, horsepower, and bollard pull have been selected as particularly relevant. Where possible, brake horsepower has been quoted for modern vessels. Indicated horsepower, which gives a larger figure, is still used by many companies in their publicity material. The relevance of this is explained in Chapter 2.

I hope that *Tugs and Towing* will convey something of the skills involved and perhaps the inherent hazards still present in the towage business. To watch tugs at work on a pleasant summer day can be misleading. The power and vast amount of energy involved, particularly when working with large ships, is not immediately apparent to the onlooker. But those same accurate manoeuvres and painstaking procedures also have to be carried out at night, in high winds, in rain, snow, and fog. An error of one metre in berthing a very large ship can bring disaster—perhaps a shattered wharf, a damaged oil pipeline, or even a national emergency. It is a tribute to tugmen world-wide that so much towage work appears to be, and is, just routine.

CHAPTER 1

Tugs: a brief history

The purpose of this chapter is briefly to trace the development of tugs from their inception to the point where the current generation of vessels began to emerge. In this way it is hoped that the present day towage scene can be considered against a background of more than 150 years of evolution.

The first tugs

Much has been written on the subject of the first practical steamship and inevitably the discussion has included the origin of the very first tug. The matter remains controversial but historians appear to agree that the first successful towing vessel made her initial trial trip in March 1802. Named the *Charlotte Dundas,* she was a very small steamboat built on the Clyde, in Scotland, to tow barges on the Forth and Clyde Canal. The trial was apparently deemed a great success but the death of her sponsor, Lord Dundas, curtailed the plans made for this little stern-wheel paddle tug.

In subsequent years a number of steam-powered passenger vessels were tried and many put into service, some with considerable success. On the other side of the Atlantic, in the United States, the passenger vessel *Claremont* was heralded as the first practical steamboat in 1807. Perhaps it is not surprising that, although these early steamers were designed primarily as passenger carrying vessels, tentative attempts were being made to tow. Dumb barges, previously towed by horses, were obvious candidates for early experimentation as were small sailing vessels, either disabled or suffering at the mercy of adverse wind conditions. Much of the towing undertaken in the first decade or two was done by small, wooden, paddle vessels operating passenger services but offering towage when an opportunity presented itself.

In Britain, the North of England and Scotland were particularly active in putting the steamboat to work. The first reference to the use of the word 'tug' is believed to have been in

*The wooden paddle tug
Industry was typical of a
great many British tugs
of the period. Her name,
too, appeared on several
early vessels. This exam-
ple was built in 1852 at
South Shields, the birth-
place on the River Tyne
of a great many tugs.
She was a vessel of 21.8
metres long and 41 gross
tons. The fragile but
graceful lines of her
planked hull and counter
stern are clearly visible.
(P. Thomas)*

connection with a small vessel designed for towing named *Tug*. This craft was built at Dumbarton in 1817 to assist ships in the Leith and Grangemouth area. In the southern ports the emphasis was still very much on passenger transport, with towage as something of a by-product.

By 1825 most major commercial ports were taking towage seriously. The advantages to the sailing ship of taking a tug for the sometimes long and difficult river passages to their dis-charging berths were becoming apparent. Previously, ships often arrived off ports and estuaries to be faced with days or even weeks of struggle against wind and tide before they could berth. In some rivers larger ships than ever before could be assisted into the main commercial areas. All of these factors had important economic connotations for the merchants and shipowners. Other industries were also beginning to see the benefits of towage. The fishing fleets and collier owners soon recognized the advantages of the steam tug. Both relied on large numbers of small sailing vessels and time was of the essence if trips were to be completed in good time and mar-kets satisfied. A single steam tug could handle several fishing craft or small colliers, taking them to sea against adverse winds or bringing them safely into port.

Across the North Sea in Europe similar advantages had been recognized. It is believed that the first steam-powered craft to be seen in Holland was a British vessel, the *Defiant*. In 1824 the States of Holland placed an order for two steam tugs for use on the Great North Holland Canal. The first, named

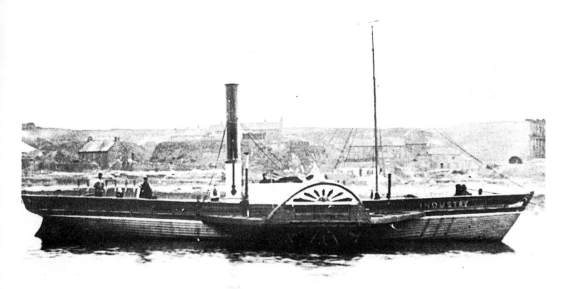

Noord Holland, went into service two years later. She was the first of several tugs to carry the name and a forerunner in what was to become a national industry of enormous importance. Much further afield, in the USA, at much the same time, the New York Dock Company commissioned the first purpose-built American tug, the *Rufus King*.

Early development

The tugs in use in the first half of the century were mostly wooden vessels with simple steam engines of just a few horse-power. They were fitted with side paddles and in many cases steered by a tiller or crude wheel and chain steering gear. Their main limitations were lack of power and phenomenal consumption of fuel and water due to the inherent inefficiency of their primitive engines and boilers. It was not unusual for them to go to work with their decks piled with coal. Their boilers worked at very low pressures and used vast amounts of fresh water. Condensers were in their infancy and if fitted at all were of a rudimentary jet type.

Another serious limitation, particularly in tugs working with ships, where manoeuvrability was already crucial, was that both paddles were usually driven by a single engine. This made the tug very difficult to handle while towing. In order to combat this problem various methods were used to vary the amount of immersion of each paddle—to give greater traction on one side or the other. One method was to fit a small truck, filled with ballast or iron chain, which ran on rails across the deck. When required the truck was moved from one side to the other, causing the tug to list and thus assist with handling the vessel. A remedy that was later to become standard in paddle tugs was to install two separate engines, one to drive each paddle. In this way the paddles could be controlled independently or locked together with a simple clutch.

The paddles themselves were the subject of much development from the very early days of steam-powered craft. The blades of the paddle wheel were known as 'floats' and were originally simple wooden components fixed rigidly to the paddle wheel. This practice was particularly inefficient. The points at which the floats entered and left the water introduced unwanted forces and drag, which seriously impaired the performance of the paddle. Those inefficiencies were multiplied the deeper the paddle was immersed. The answer to this problem emerged in the form of the 'feathering' float. A simple mechanism was introduced that enabled the angle of each float to be changed automatically as the paddle rotated. In this way each float entered and left the water vertically, ensuring that the thrust produced was horizontal and drag reduced to a minimum. This had the added bonus that the

United was a classic British paddle tug of wooden construction built in 1873. She had many features in common with tugs built in iron and steel. Her dimensions were 27.05 metres long, 5.56 metres beam, 2.84 metres draft, and 87 tons gross. United had a host of owners on the north-east coast of Britain and remained in service until she was scrapped by her last owner, France, Fenwick Tyne & Wear Company, in 1927. (P. Thomas)

depth of immersion of the paddle, which varied with the draft of the vessel, did not have such a marked effect on performance. Feathering mechanisms became standard on paddle tugs within the first decade or so and by the middle of the nineteenth century an established design was to emerge which became universal on paddle-driven craft.

As previously mentioned, the very early tugs were of wooden construction. Their hulls were mostly clincher-built with fine lines and a graceful appearance. They were, however, relatively fragile craft, working in an environment which easily led to serious damage. Problems also arose as more powerful engines were developed. Stronger hulls became necessary to resist the considerable forces generated by the propulsion systems. In a tug this posed a greater problem than in most early steam-powered craft. Constant manoeuvring tended to cause movement in the timbers of wooden tugs, leading to constant leaking and the danger of sinking if left unattended. The introduction of iron as a suitable material for ship construction eventually resolved this dilemma. There is some uncertainty as to the actual date the first iron tug was introduced, but 1841 is often quoted. It is known that several vessels using this method of construction were in use by 1850. Wrought iron, the malleable material actually used for much of the structure in shipbuilding, was particularly well suited for the purpose. It absorbed a great deal of punishment and stood up well to the marine environment.

Paddle versus screw propeller

The introduction of the screw propeller and the events that led to its adoption are well documented in the vast range of shipping history books. The consequences of those events had a profound effect on every aspect of the shipping industry, including the development of tugs. Experiments with the Archimedean screw took place for some years before culminating in the famous 'tug of war' between the *Alecto* and *Rattler* in 1845. This demonstration was organized by the British Admiralty to determine conclusively which of the available propulsion methods was in fact the most efficient. The two vessels were wooden steam-powered sloops, similar in dimensions and of recent construction. *Rattler* was fitted with a screw propeller, the *Alecto* with paddles. A number of free-running speed trials were carried out over several days in the North Sea. The trials ended with a tug of war in which the two vessels were tethered stern to stern. The overall victor was the *Rattler*. In the towing trial she succeeded in pulling the *Alecto* along stern first at some $2^{1}/_{2}$ miles per hour. Four years later the Admiralty repeated the trial with two more vessels, the *Niger* and *Basilisk,* and again the screw-propelled ship proved superior.

These famous trials set the scene quite conclusively in naval circles and the parent shipping industry, but tug operators were—and still are—a particularly fickle breed. Many turned their backs on the screw for many years but others were quick to adopt the new propeller. In towage, the paddle had many advantages. Generally, the draft of a paddle tug could be kept shallow, which was a useful feature in many developing ports. Once twin, independently controlled, engines became established the paddle tug became extremely agile. The turning force that could be exerted by going ahead on one paddle and astern on the other was considerable and was put to good use in shiphandling.

It is not surprising that the major navies took a great interest in the development of tugs and towage. Obviously, large fleets of warships, either under sail or using early steam power, were vulnerable to weather and tidal conditions when entering port or operating in coastal waters. The British Admiralty have, since those very early days, operated large tug fleets and developed vessels to fulfil their own particular needs. It is also interesting to note that their fleets contained both screw and paddle driven vessels until as recently as the 1970s.

The industry becomes established

By the middle of the nineteenth century tug fleets as we now know them were rapidly becoming established. Competition among the various operators was fierce, resulting in considerable bargaining between individual owners, owner/skippers, and clients. Inevitably, companies were formed to reduce this competition and pool resources. In many ports companies providing other services to shipping, such as agency and stevedoring, also went into the towage business. As previously mentioned, the ports in the North of England and Scotland were among the first to develop towage services and small fleets were quickly established.

Further south, the famous Thames company, William Watkins Ltd, was formed in 1833 with the second-hand paddle tug *Monarch*. This little tug was a wooden craft of only 64 feet 10 inches (19.76 metres) in length powered by a single engine rated at 20 nominal horsepower. She remained with the firm for many years, being continually modernized and refitted. The company's first purpose-built vessel, the *Fiddler*, was delivered in 1840, to be followed by a whole succession of tugs stretching over the next 135 years.

In the same year, in France, La Siciétié Bertin, forerunners to the 'Les Abeille' fleet, began operation in the Le Havre area with small steam-powered vessels of between 50 and 140 horsepower. The Compagnie de Remorquage Les Abeilles, was founded in 1867 with the tugs *Abeille No 1* and *No 2*. The Les Abeilles fleet ('The Bees') still operates in Le Havre and other neighbouring ports, albeit under the umbrella of a large parent group.

In Holland the now world-famous Smit fleet started operation in 1842 with their first paddle tug the *Kinderdijk*. She was a 140 horsepower tug put into service to assist sailing vessels on route between Rotterdam and the North Sea. During the following years this fleet developed rapidly, employing in the early days both screw- and paddle-driven vessels. Their paddle tug *Wodan*, introduced in 1870, was their first seagoing tug. By the turn of the century this company was already among the leaders in deep sea long-range towage.

Denmark also has a towage company that can be traced back to the mid 1800s. The Svitzer towage and salvage concern was formed in 1854. Their first vessel was the steamer *Loven*, built in 1835 for the Danish Ministry of Naval Affairs. After a while it was decided that she was more suited to passenger and cargo use and was replaced by a former British steamship, the *Freja*, described as a tug/packet steamer. A similar pattern was gradually emerging in most major ports in Europe and North America.

Extending the range

During the first forty years or so the range of most of the tugs in service was painfully short, for the reasons already mentioned. Coastal voyages took place but were only generally undertaken to transfer tugs from port to port. Towing any distance from the tug's home port was quite a different matter. It was not unheard of for an early tug, working with a ship, to borrow coal from the ship in order to be able to complete the job, so poor was their fuel consumption. By mid century considerable progress had been made to improve this situation. Tugs were becoming larger, more powerful, with improvements in engine and boiler design; they were also more economical in both water and coal. Many of these later tugs were considerably larger, some exceeding 100 feet (39 metres) in length, with a gross registered tonnage of perhaps 150 tons.

Such vessels were often fitted with more than one boiler. In Britain it was quite common for each boiler to be given a separate funnel. Two boilers, with twin funnels side by side, were quite normal and three or even four not unheard of. By using this multiple boiler arrangement the vessel was made more powerful for towing but when running light one or more boiler could be closed down. In this way fuel was saved and, by banking up the boilers not being used, steam could be quickly raised when required. During the middle years of the nineteenth century the majority of larger seagoing tugs were still paddle-driven vessels. Other refinements were also emerging. Improvements in steering gear were introduced and steam-operated anchor windlasses took the backbreaking effort out of raising anchors to get underway.

There was considerable commercial inducement for the tug owner to extend the useful range of his vessels. Steam-driven ships were becoming more numerous and in order to compete effectively the sailing ship captain was frequently obliged to resort to the use of a tug. This was often the only way of delivering valuable cargoes in time for particular markets. Again, the port of London was a good example. A sailing ship, without assistance, could take days or even weeks to complete the 36-mile journey upriver from the open sea. By the 1850s tugs were being put into service that could not only tow these ships

Renown was an iron paddle tug typical of many used for 'seeking' duties from the River Thames. She was constructed in 1863 at Deptford and operated very successfully by William Watkins & Son. A relatively shallow draft enabled her to perform a number of salvage operations, saving ships aground in the English Channel. She was a tug of 165 tons gross. Twin funnels were a common feature in tugs of her type.

to and from their berths in London but also undertake much longer tows. Journeys were being made between ports with ships in tow. And although it was considered a feat, the first trips across the English Channel were being made with vessels in tow. It was also becoming possible to move other floating objects between ports by using tugs.

Seeking

Once longer distance tows could be undertaken reliably 'seeking' began. The term seeking was used universally to describe the activities of a tug searching at sea for an incoming ship to tow into port. This activity became an important source of revenue for the tug owner and probably reached its peak around 1865–70. By 1865 many tugs were available with sufficient range to enable them to travel long distances to meet homeward-bound sailing ships. A tug would leave its home port with a ship in tow, taking her out to the open sea. In the case of London this might be well out into the Thames estuary or down the English Channel, sometimes as far as Land's End. The tug would then seek out a home-coming ship in the hope of finding a tow for the return passage.

The fee for this service was negotiated 'on the spot', resulting in a verbal agreement struck between the tug captain and the master of the ship. These negotiations were not always resolved quickly. If the ship's captain was reluctant to pay for a tow, the tug might lay nearby waiting for weather conditions to deteriorate and the potential client to change his mind. It is recorded that on one occasion the captain of an Australian clipper ship refused a tow from off the Eddystone lighthouse to London for the very reasonable sum (even in those days) of £50. The tug master refused to accept a sum of £30 offered. The ship made reasonable progress up the Channel to the North Foreland. There she was forced to take a tug but was by that time in company with several other ships, all in need of tugs. Eventually, the master had to pay £60 to be towed the much shorter distance.

Competition was fierce, with perhaps more than one tug trying to strike a bargain. Tugs would race each other to contact the master of a likely ship. In some areas, an unwritten rule dictated that once a tug captain made contact with the ship's master there would be no further interference. Tug crews often took out with them recent newspapers, fresh food, and similar items which would be popular aboard a sailing ship that had been at sea for many weeks. Such inducements did not overcome commercial considerations but no doubt the sight of a tug was often a welcome one to the crew of a home-coming ship.

A similar pattern of seeking operations was emerging in most major shipping areas, both in Europe and North

America. Seeking became an important activity for tug and ship owners alike and was to continue for many decades, until the days of the commercial sailing ship were virtually finished. There is no doubt that seeking also made a significant impact on tug development. The continuing need to improve economy, range, and sea-keeping qualities produced changes that eventually affected all types of tug.

Deep sea towing

In present towage circles deep sea towing is taken to mean any towage operation outside coastal waters and excluding short sea crossings. This now includes voyages to any part of the world, towing ships of all sizes and sometimes floating structures of immense size. By the 1870s such towing operations, on a much smaller scale, were just becoming a reality.

There was an obvious need to tow ships long distances, either steam ships with defective machinery or sailing ships requiring assistance for commercial reasons. Dredging equipment and similar unwieldy objects were built for export in many major industrial centres but delivery had previously presented difficult and sometimes insurmountable problems. A natural extension of seeking was full deep sea operation.

One of the first tugs to undertake true deep sea towage was the London tug *Anglia*. She was a paddle tug built in 1866 for William Watkins Ltd and was for some years the most powerful tug in the world. Her paddles were driven by engines producing 700 indicated horsepower. Three boilers provided steam for the engines, each with its own funnel. Her coal bunkers were said at the time to be the largest ever fitted in a tug. *Anglia* started work as a seeking tug but was soon to become famous for her feats in long-distance towing. In 1875 she made history by towing a disabled liner, the *Syria*, from St

Many early tugs had very long working lives. The Lingdale *was built in 1882 by Westwood Bailie & Co of London for the Dover Harbour Board, bearing the original name* Lady Vita. *She became the* Lingdale *in 1914 on joining the fleet of the Tees Towing Company Ltd for use in Middlesbrough. Her career ended when she was scrapped in 1954. She was a vessel of 174 tons gross and 32.79 metres in length.* (P. Thomas)

19

The paddler Wodan was the first oceangoing tug to be operated by L. Smit of Rotterdam, the fore-runners of the present Smit-Tak organization. She was built in 1883 but did not venture much further than the English Channel and German Bight. (Smit International)

Helena to Southampton. Among her other successes was the delivery of Cleopatra's Needle to London in 1878. It had been towed, in a specially constructed floating container, from Alexandria by a steamship but broke adrift off the coast of Spain. The container was later found by Spanish fishermen. *Anglia* was sent to Ferrol to complete the job of taking the obelisk to the Thames. In spite of this famous and successful exploit, *Anglia* was already becoming outmoded. Her owners, along with many others, had started to take the screw pro-peller seriously. They were building tugs with screw propulsion that were proving both powerful and economical to operate. Such vessels rapidly made their mark in long-range towing.

The Dutch paddle tug *Wodan* has already been mentioned. She was introduced in 1870 and ventured from her home port of Rotterdam as far as the English Channel and the German Bight. Her owners, L. Smit, were quick to turn to the screw propeller in subsequent seagoing tugs. This they did with great success, making enormous progress by the end of the century.

The crews

No account of these early days of towing would be complete without mentioning the men involved and the conditions in which they worked. Whether in port or at sea, towage was a hazardous business. Even the more advanced tugs were primi-tive by present-day standards, with little protection for the crews from weather or sea. The coal-fired boilers consumed vast amounts of fuel, all of which had to be taken aboard, stowed in the bunkers, and later fed into the boilers by hand. A seagoing vessel underway at speed or towing could easily use in excess of 10 tons in a day, all of which had to be moved by shovel in a cramped, hot boiler room aboard a tug subject to all the pitching and rolling movements normal for a small vessel in a seaway.

On deck, work continued in all weathers. The tow ropes were often huge, manufactured from manila or sisal and very difficult to handle. These ropes were enormously heavy, particularly once they had become soaked in water. The task of making a towing connection with a sailing ship at sea, possibly in winter, can only be imagined. Even in harbour tugs the crews frequently lived aboard, working long hours with little opportunity to spend time at home.

Much of the success of those early tugs can be attributed to the tug masters, often better known as 'skippers'. They developed skills in handling their vessels second to none. There was a need to work in close proximity to ships, in a variety of circumstances and sometimes in appalling weather conditions. This ran contrary to established maritime practice where the golden rule demanded plenty of 'sea room'. An intimate knowledge of the tug's handling characteristics, tides, winds, and local conditions were a necessity for every master. In addition, it was necessary to maintain a high level of discipline on board to ensure that work was carried out correctly. Failure on the part of a crew member while working on deck or in the engine room could endanger the tug and possibly her tow.

The engineer aboard a tug had a very important role to play in the operation of the vessel. His function was not simply one of keeping the machinery working smoothly and reliably. The engineer and his staff 'drove' the engines. Communication between the master and the engineer was via the time-honoured engine-room telegraph, which indicated by means of bells and indicators the required manoeuvres. A voice pipe was used in addition to enable special instructions to be conveyed direct. Skippers and engineers often developed an

Triton is another name borne by many tugs. This British vessel was a single-screw tug built at Falmouth in 1883. She was a vessel of only 75 tons gross and 25.6 metres in length, seen here in the livery of the Anchor Steam Tug Co Ltd of Newcastle. Triton had a number of owners and finished her days shortly before the Second World War in the John Davies tug fleet in Cardiff.

exceptional rapport. By means of special signals a skipper might order just a single turn of the propeller or a paddle, either ahead or astern, to assist in a delicate manoeuvre. The engineer and his fireman also needed to anticipate in advance when a demand would be made for extra power. In that way the boilers were kept suitably stoked in readiness so that steam pressure did not fail at the critical moment.

Many of the skills learnt in those early days continued to develop and remain with the industry today. Work in tugs has tended to run in families, with skills and knowhow passed down from father to son, often within the same firm. A large number of the tug skippers and crewmen in today's fleets can trace their ancestry back through several generations in the towage business.

The turn of the century

The turn of the century represented an interesting milestone in the history of tugs and towage. The last couple of decades of the nineteenth century saw considerable consolidation in the industry. Various basic tug types had evolved, in forms which were in many ways to remain largely unchanged for at least another half century. Indeed a small number of vessels put into service in the late nineteenth and early twentieth centuries are still in existence in various parts of the world.

Screw propellers had ousted the paddle in many applications by 1900. In small river tugs, used for barge towing work, the screw had been quickly adopted as the more practical propulsion system. The width and vulnerability of paddles were soon recognized as a distinct disadvantage in that role. Likewise in deep sea towing, the early popularity of

The little wooden steam tug Princess May *was originally built in Hull in 1893 for a foreign owner but was purchased almost immediately by a British company. Subsequent owners operated her in London, Ipswich, and Scarborough. She measured 22.6 metres in length and 43 tons gross.*
(P. Thomas)

the paddle waned in favour of the screw, once development of the propeller was further advanced. The vastly superior fuel economy possible with screw tugs did much to influence owners. Engine design had moved towards the compound and triple expansion types and massive advances had been made in the development of condensers.

Adoption of the screw propeller in the smaller shiphandling and harbour tug generally was still mixed. In Britain, some ports retained their paddle tugs for many years. In the rest of Europe and America paddle-driven tugs disappeared quite rapidly. Significant exceptions were inland waterways craft used for towing or pushing barges on rivers and canals. In this application side or stern paddles were to remain in use for some time, to help minimize the vessel's draft.

European designs are established

In Britain, in 1900, the 'state-of-the-art' harbour and coastal tug was a vessel of some 100-200 tons gross. She was propelled, more often than not, by a single screw propeller and engines producing between 400 and 1,000 indicated horsepower. The configuration that had become established was one that was to change very little until alternative propulsion systems emerged long after the Second World War.

Most British tugs were fitted with towing hooks as a means of securing the towrope. In Europe some countries used hooks and others a simple bollard arrangement. The advantage of the towing hook is that some means of quick release can be incorporated to enable the towrope to be released, should the need arise. A distinctive feature of British and European tugs is the location of the towing hooks or bollards. They are normally positioned just aft of amidships. This allows the tug to

South Cock was typical of a British shiphandling tug of her time. She was a single-screw steam tug of 600 indicated horsepower, built in 1904 for use by the Liverpool Screw Towing Co Ltd. Her principal dimensions were 29.3 metres long, 6.7 metres beam, 3.4 metres draft and 149 tons gross. These were regarded as 'standard' measurements for tugs working in the docks and entrance locks in the Mersey area. She remained in service until 1959.

This picture of the steam tug Beatrice Bush *shows a typical American configuration, with a long deckhouse and towing bollards placed well aft. Note the heavy fendering to protect the tug as she worked alongside. Her main employment was working with railway barges. The tug was owned by the Bush Terminal Company of New York and was built in 1905. She was a vessel of 212 tons gross and 750 indicated horsepower.*

manoeuvre easily whilst towing. The further aft and nearer the rudder the tow is secured, the more difficult it is for the tug to turn. This arrangement requires a long clear after deck with the superstructure located well forward, a feature identifying tugs with a strong European influence.

Seagoing tugs had developed considerably by the turn of the century. They were obviously larger vessels, designed to spend long periods at sea and capable of withstanding the stresses of poor wind and sea conditions. The power output of their engines and the efficiency of the boilers had also improved, resulting in much better fuel consumption. A rating of 1,500 indicated horsepower was not uncommon. Power-operated deck equipment was in regular use and on some vessels included relatively simple steam towing winches. The British lead in deep sea towing was already being seriously challenged by Dutch companies. Large powerful tugs were owned by L. Smit of Rotterdam, and other firms that were to become world leaders in the field were building large numbers of advanced seagoing tugs.

A different approach in America

Development in North America had followed a similar pattern, but some significant differences in design emerged which remain evident in conventional screw tugs even today. Powerful screw tugs were well established both in harbour and at sea by 1900.

Again, the position and type of towing gear was, and remains, a distinctive feature. Tow ropes were generally secured to towing bollards but these were positioned much further aft. This was made possible by the towing methods used, particularly when working with ships in harbour. Much less direct towing is employed. The tug is often secured alongside the ship or by a rope from her bow. Towing astern in the normal way is still carried out but under circumstances where manoeuvrability is less likely to be affected. These factors significantly affected the configuration of the American tug. A much longer superstructure is possible, with more accommodation at main deck level, giving a profile quite different from the European breed.

In America the use of tugs also developed quickly in other respects. Tug services set up originally to render assistance to the large fleets of coastal schooners soon gave way to tug and barge services operating on the same routes. Tugs and barges were engaged in a number of regular services by the turn of the century. Most of the cargoes were bulk commodities such as coal, stone, gravel, and building materials. On the east coast of North America some of the routes were quite long, extending down into the Gulf of Mexico. One seasonal cargo was ice, transported from the north down to the southern ports and as far as Cuba. The tugs engaged on these services were efficient vessels of between 120 and 140 feet (36.5 and 42.6 metres) in length with engines of 850–1,000 horsepower. In later years tug and barge services were to develop considerably, covering most of the American coastline, extending across the Pacific and north to Alaska.

Another aspect of American towage that was quite unique was the use of tugs by various railway companies. Specially adapted barges were developed to carry railway rolling stock across many of the larger harbours and rivers. Several such services were established by 1900 and some remain in use. The tugs used were very similar to the ship-handling vessels of the period. Most of the towing was done 'alongside', except on the very long routes where bad weather could make it too dangerous. In many cases railway tugs did not have condensers fitted

The Dutch oceangoing tug Noordzee *illustrates the progress made in tugs of that type towards the end of the century. She was constructed in 1892 for L. Smit of Rotterdam and performed many long distance voyages, including tows to South America. A tug of some 228 registered tons, she had steam machinery of 750 indicated horsepower. Note the furled sails, which were used to obtain some assistance from the wind when circumstances permitted.*

to enable boiler water to be reused. Supplies of water and coal were plentiful at the railway depots and the routes generally quite short, so the expense of a condenser was regarded as unnecessary.

Obviously some deep sea towage and salvage work took place around the North American seaboard. Due to the coastal trade there were many tugs available capable of lengthy tows. The American industry did not show the same level of interest in world-wide towage operations as did their counterparts in Europe.

The First World War (1914–18)

Although tugs had been used to a limited degree in some earlier conflicts, the First World War was to highlight the importance of such vessels in wartime. It was the first highly mechanized wartime scenario, involving very large numbers of steam-driven ships and the transportation of vast amounts of men and supplies by sea.

The demand for tugs was enormous. They were required to provide towage services in extremely busy ports, where they were in constant use berthing and moving ships at the various stages of loading, unloading, and preparation for sea. Ships were also being damaged and sunk at an unprecedented rate. There was tremendous pressure to recover damaged ships, carry out repairs, and get them back into service as quickly as possible. In order to achieve this it was necessary to have sufficient tugs available that were capable of carrying out search and rescue operations. These activities were carried out by a wide variety of tugs, both in coastal waters and much further afield.

An additional need was for tugs to tow barges loaded with men and equipment. This method of transport was used not only across the English Channel, from Britain to the continent of Europe, but also to move such supplies inland through the waterways system. Tugs were also used by the inspection services—where sturdy, seaworthy vessels were needed to go alongside ships entering port areas to check documents, nationalities, etc. Numerous other duties included work at defensive harbour booms and patrolling the major fleet anchorages.

These demands were met in a number of ways. The naval authorities initially requisitioned a large number of tugs from commercial owners to supplement their own fleets. In many ways this was counter-productive. Many of the tugs were taken from ports that were already under great pressure from the increased wartime shipping traffic. Requisitioned vessels from the British fleets were used extensively alongside their naval cousins, some working as far afield as Gallipoli, the

Dardanelles, and Archangel.

A number of building programmes were started in order to increase the number of tugs available. High on the list of priorities were rescue and salvage tugs. The British Admiralty placed orders for several large tugs. It was already becoming common practice for naval tugs to be built in 'classes' of several almost identical vessels. Among the new tugs built for wartime service were the three 'Frisky' class, twin-screw, seagoing vessels of 155 feet (47.2 metres) in length powered by two steam engines producing a total of 1,200 horsepower. An improved and much larger version known as the 'R' class were 186 feet (56.7 metres) in length and had twice the power. Both types were extensively fitted out for salvage work and had impressive twin funnels.

By far the most prolific programme was that which produced the 'Saint' class tugs. Forty-six tugs were built with names prefixed 'Saint'. They were single-screw seagoing vessels of 135 feet (41.15 metres) in length. A triple expansion main engine of some 1,250 horsepower was installed. Many of the tugs used for rescue and salvage work and convoy escort duty were armed, including some of the requisitioned vessels. A variety of guns were fitted for self protection, ranging from a 12-pounder mounted on the forecastle to machine guns on the wings of the bridge. The larger tugs engaged in rescue and escort duties were among the first to be fitted with radio-telephony equipment. It was to be many years before the smaller harbour tug was to be so equipped as a matter of course.

Other, smaller, types of tug were also included in the wartime building programmes. Many of these are not shown in naval records but were identified by numbers with prefixes, HS, AS, ATT, and similar. They were of wooden, steel, and in one class concrete construction. These vessels were used to supplement the fleets of ship-handling tugs and carry out a

Saint Monance was one of 46 tugs of her type laid down for use in the First World War by the British Admiralty. This example was actually constructed in the Hong Kong & Whampoa Dockyard but not completed until 1919. Much of her subsequent career was spent as a rescue tug based at Portsmouth. She was finally sold in 1948.
(J. W. Kennedy/WSS)

whole host of duties in Britain and overseas on the inland waterways. In the USA a series of 48 tugs and barges were built by the United States Shipping Board to support the war effort. These were tugs of 142 feet (43.3 metres) in length with steam engines of 800 horsepower.

A great many of the tugs intended for war service were not completed in time, including the majority of the 'Saints'. As a result, after hostilities ceased, a large number of vessels of all types became available for commercial use. Surplus smaller vessels quickly found employment in commercial harbour fleets and among barge operators. Of the 'Saints', a large proportion were sold or chartered to commercial operators for deep sea towing and proved very successful. It is interesting to note that many of those were recalled to naval service in the Second World War.

Between the wars

The period between the world wars was in some respects a strange one for the towage industry. Although the First World War produced no massive technological advances it provided the industry with many modern vessels and a considerable amount of useful operating experience. Very soon after the war, in the early 1920s, the world-wide economic recession affected all aspects of the shipping business, including towage. During the period of recession and into the 1930s little significant change took place in basic tug design but owners were forced to look seriously at reducing running costs.

Oil versus coal
Adopting an alternative fuel was the means used by owners in

The 'Sun Tugs' of W.H.J. Alexander Ltd were famous in the London area. Sun XV *was a single-screw steam tug of 750 indicated horsepower built in Hull by Earle & Company in 1925. A tug of 183 tons gross, she remained coal fired until after the Second World War. Her career ended in 1969 when she was sold for scrap. She was one of several Thames tugs that helped in the evacuation of the British Army from Dunkirk in 1940.* (Author)

some parts of the world to reduce running costs. In the United States the relatively simple expedient of using oil fuel in steam tugs quickly became popular. The use of oil was not, however, universal and depended very much on the relative prices of oil and coal in the area and the trade in which the tug was employed.

In Britain and Europe coal was to remain the fuel for the vast majority of tugs until well into the Second World War. Coal was readily available in most ports and oil was rather more expensive than in the USA. Oil was without doubt a much more convenient fuel, offering the advantages of much reduced labour in the boiler room and clean, easy bunkering.

Diesel power

Again it was the USA that led the way in the development of diesel-powered tugs. As early as the 1920s the diesel engine was being used as an alternative to steam, particularly in small vessels. Diesel engines were proving to be extremely economic to run, bearing in mind the relatively low cost of oil fuels in the USA. Here also was a significant saving in manpower. No stoker or fireman was required and no fuel was used to keep boilers warm when the tug was not in use. When the tug was required for work the engine was started and the vessel could be underway immediately, without the hinderance of waiting to raise steam. The power to weight and size ratios were also seen as a great advantage. Diesel engines of similar power took up much less space than steam machinery giving greater flexibility in design. By the 1930s increasing numbers of American tugs were being built with diesel engines and a decade later were well accepted by the industry as a whole.

On the other side of the Atlantic the situation was quite different. British owners were certainly reluctant to consider the

The American tug Humrick was originally constructed as a steam vessel in 1919 but converted to diesel power. A large vessel of some 418 tons, she was given a General Motors engine of 850 bhp. Humrick is shown in the colours of the Crescent Towage & Salvage Co of New Orleans.

The first British attempt to produce a diesel-electric shiphandling tug was the Acklam Cross. *When she was built in 1933 for the Tees Towing Company she embodied several new features. A vessel of 150 tons gross and 600 horsepower, she remained in service in Middlesbrough until 1964 when she was sold for further use in Malta and eventually lost in 1969.* (Tees Towing)

diesel engine seriously for other than very small tugs. There are a number of factors that led to the late adoption of the diesel engine in the British and European towage industries. The economics of diesel fuel were certainly less of an incentive than in the USA, but there were also features concerned with the operation of diesel-powered vessels that were not easily reconciled. By their nature, diesel engines were required to run at relatively high speeds in order to achieve their optimum power output. In order to turn the propeller shaft at a suitable speed gearing was needed and this was not popular. The owners of ship-handling tugs in particular were keen to have vessels that handled and could be operated like a steam tug. Deeply immersed, slowly rotating propellers that could be very accurately controlled were the features required. This was not easily achieved with the diesel engine.

There were a number of ways of overcoming the shortcomings of the early diesel engine. One, introduced in the USA and still popular there, was to have a diesel-electric propulsion system. The engine is coupled to a generator and runs at a constant speed. An electric motor drives the propeller shaft using current produced by the generator. This arrangement gives a very high degree of control but is relatively expensive to install. The system was first tried in Britain in the new tug *Acklam Cross* built in 1933 for use on the River Tees. She was a ship-handling tug of 150 tons gross with two 300-horsepower diesel generators supplying current to a single propeller motor. Due to her electric drive her propeller could be controlled directly from the bridge, a feature considered revolutionary at the time. Although she worked successfully, very few British tugs were built with diesel-electric systems.

A more common British solution, introduced in the 1930s, was the slow-running direct-reversing diesel engine. This type of engine was to become widely used after the Second World War and many examples still remain in operation. The engine is a comparatively large diesel coupled directly to the tug's propeller shaft and capable of running as slow as 70 revolutions per minute. A compressed air system is used to start the engine. To go astern, the engine is stopped, automatically retimed, and restarted to rotate in the opposite direction. This unlikely sounding arrangement works well in practice. A disadvantage is the need for a substantial supply of compressed air. A tug master finding it necessary to make a large number of forward and astern movements has been known to run short of air and be faced with an engine that would not restart at the critical moment.

One of the best known engines of the direct reversing type was the British Polar diesel. Early models were rated between 350 and 600 brake horsepower (bhp) and ran at approximately 70-300 rpm. These were mainly installed in barge tugs and the smaller harbour vessels. Engines from the same manufacturer were later to power much larger tugs with horsepowers exceeding 1,600 bhp.

The Kort nozzle

In 1932 a device was invented in Germany by a Herr Kort which, quite by accident, was to have a far-reaching effect on tug performance in the years to come. The banks of German canals were suffering from serious erosion problems caused by the use of increasingly powerful tugs to tow barges. Herr

Khurdah was one of the first practical British diesel tugs, built for use on the Thames and Medway in 1930. She was owned by J.P. Knight Ltd of Rochester and fitted with a direct-reversing British Polar diesel engine of 495 bhp. Khurdah seen here towing Thames lighters, was eventually scrapped in 1982. (Author)

Kort, an aerodynamicist, was given the task of designing a shroud to contain the effects of wash from the tug's propeller. His shroud was a fixed tubular structure that completely surrounded the propeller. It had the desired effect but it was quickly discovered that there was also a marked increase in the tug's towing performance.

Tests were carried out with models and eventually a towing trial was held, using two similar tugs, on the Mitteland canal. In this trial a small tug with a 120 horsepower engine and fitted with the new Kort nozzle successfully beat a 180 horsepower vessel in a 'tug of war' contest. It was subsequently found that in larger steam tugs an increase in static pull — what is now known as bollard pull — of up to 50 per cent was possible. In the early days the nozzle was a fixed device surrounding the propeller and attached to the vessel's structure. In later years fully steerable nozzle rudders were to be developed, improving the tug's handling characteristics considerably. The Kort nozzle was first introduced into Britain in 1934 but was not adopted extensively there or elsewhere in the world until the 1950s.

The Second World War

The Second World War was to place much greater demand on tugs and the towing services than the previous conflict. The increased use of submarine warfare, aerial bombing, and the need to keep supply traffic moving put incredible pressure on the whole shipping industry. Along with the subsequent invasion of Europe, with huge amounts of material being transported by sea, the need for tugs of all types was unprecedented. Commercial vessels were requisitioned as in the First World War but extensive building programmes were required to meet the demands of all the various users. Again the emphasis was on 'standard types' that could be produced quickly. A full account of all the various types of wartime tugs, their design and uses, would fill a complete volume. There are however aspects of towage during this period that are particularly important in the evolution of the tug as we know it.

Oceangoing tugs

The huge shipping losses sustained throughout the war made rescue and salvage particularly important. Where possible many shipping convoys were provided with tugs as part of their naval escort. The large numbers of suitable oceangoing tugs required for these services came from many sources. Among the several classes of tug built for the British Admiralty, for rescue and salvage work, were a great many steam-powered vessels. The first of these were the 'Assurance' type, a class of 21 vessels of 156 feet (47.5 metres) in length and

630 tons gross. Some of these were put into service as early as 1940 and were to bear the brunt of much of the escort and rescue work. Later in the war five larger 'Envoy' class tugs, of a very similar design, were to be built for the same purpose.

Perhaps the most significant class of oceangoing tug introduced in wartime were the 'Bustlers'. They were the first diesel tugs of any size built for the Admiralty and their design had much in common with the famous Dutch tug *Zwarte Zee* introduced in 1933. Eight of the type were built, with the name ship of the class, *Bustler*, entering service in 1942. They were 205 feet (62.5 metres) in length and 1,100 tons gross. Two Atlas Polar diesel engines produced a total of 3,020 bhp and were coupled, through a gearbox, to a single propeller. *Bustler* and her sisters had a range of 5,000 miles at 12 knots and a bollard pull of 30 tons. This performance made them particularly useful as long-range rescue tugs.

A considerable number of oceangoing tugs were also built for the war effort on the other side of the Atlantic in the USA. Of these about thirty were supplied to Britain under a lend/lease agreement. The majority were twin screw and fitted with diesel-electric propulsion systems. Due to wartime shortages of raw materials wood was used extensively in America for tugs of all types, including the larger deep sea types.

The 'Empires'

One major step taken by the British government to rectify the shortage of tugs, for a wide range of applications, was the introduction of the 'Empire' tug building programme. The Ministry of War Transport placed a succession of orders for tugs ranging from medium-sized ship-handling types to vessels capable of coastal towing and deep sea work. All were steam-powered single-screw vessels. The basic designs were

Bustler was the name ship of the famous wartime class of rescue and fleet tugs. Powered by two Atlas-Polar diesel engines driving a single screw, she was rated at 3,020 bhp with a bollard pull of 30 tons. She operated as a fleet and rescue tug in wartime and was chartered out for commercial use in the post-war period, remaining in Naval service until her sale to Yugoslavia in 1973. (Author)

Photographs of the 'Empire' class vessels in their wartime garb are rare. Empire Palm is seen here in her original Ministry of War Transport livery. She was built in 1942 on the Clyde by Scott & Sons Ltd at Bowling — a ship-handling tug of 260 tons gross and 32.6 metres in length. After the war she was sold to the Ardrossan Harbour Company in Scotland as the Seaway, *where she worked until 1969.* (Graham Langmuir)

developed from those of successful commercial vessels built and in service before the war. Various shipyards were made responsible for certain types and in all 145 tugs were produced to a dozen designs. It is interesting to note that a very large proportion of the tugs were built with oil-fired boilers; of the others, many were converted to this more convenient fuel after quite a short time.

All of the tugs were named using the 'Empire' prefix. Some vessels were allocated to naval authorities and others placed under the management of commercial operators. The deployment took tugs of the Empire classes to any part of the world where they could be usefully employed, including Africa and the Far East. In the early post-war years many of these tugs were to play an important part in the development of new and existing towage concerns.

Small tugs

Very much smaller tugs were also included in the wartime building programme. One of the largest classes of tug ever to be constructed was the British 'TID' type. These were small steam tugs of only 70 feet (21.3 metres) in length overall, powered by a single two-cylinder engine producing 220 horsepower. The need for such a vessel was identified in 1942 and the resources had to be found to enable building to proceed. Shipbuilding capacity was already heavily committed to larger and more important vessels. This led to a programme being initiated, by the Admiralty Merchant Shipbuilding Department, to 'design, organise and start work immediately towards achieving, in the shortest possible time, the delivery of one tug per week, using in the process, little or no shipyard labour'.

The tugs were built to a standard design developed to be assembled from prefabricated sections. The hull was a welded structure, designed to eliminate the need for complicated plate rolling or shaping. Each tug hull was made up of eight sections. Every section had to be capable of being transported by road. This enabled the various sections to be constructed by companies capable of welded steel fabrication work but not necessarily with any shipbuilding experience. In the initial stages the design work and final assembly was carried out by a single company, the Humberside shipbuilder Richard Dunstons Ltd. The orders for this little tug were progressively increased from a dozen to the 182 vessels of the type that were actually completed. During the periods of maximum production three tugs per week were being delivered. All carried the initials 'TID' and a number instead of a name. The numbers ran from 1 to 183—there was no number 13. The origin of 'TID' remains obscure but it was almost certainly an abbreviation of 'Tug Invasion Duty'.

The first tug entered service in 1943 and was one of 90 coal-fired vessels. The need to operate overseas made oil firing an essential modification and all subsequent tugs were built to use oil fuel. 'TID' tugs were widely used in just about every application they were capable of fulfilling. Batches of tugs were loaded aboard ships and transported to ports in the Far East. During the invasion of France many of the tugs were used to assist in placing the temporary harbours. Their relatively shallow draft enabled them to perform a host of duties including, as the war progressed, work on the inland waterways in Europe.

There were two other classes of small harbour tug built in

The 182 'TID' class tugs were built to carry out a multitude of duties during the Second World War. TID 3 was one of the very first, coal-fired vessels, built in 1943. She remained in naval service for the whole of her working life, until finally being scrapped in 1973. The tug is seen here working at Portsmouth naval base. Note the spark arrestor guard fitted to her funnel, a device used on steam tugs working with ammunition barges to reduce the risk of fire. (Author)

large numbers and worthy of mention. These were the 'TANACs' and 'TUSAs'. Both classes were of very similar in size and power to the 'TIDs' but diesel powered. The 'TANAC' tugs were built in Canada in large numbers and shipped to Britain and many other locations around the world. Another American lend/lease scheme produced the 'TUSA' type of tug. These were wooden tugs allocated mainly for use in Australia and the Far East.

The early post-war years

At the end of the war there was, on the one hand, an enormous surplus of tugs of all types but, on the other, a great deal of work to be done. A large number of tugs were laid up pending disposal. Others were allocated to vast clearing-up operations, often working on loan or charter to civilian firms. They were involved in salvaging the many wrecks remaining in harbours and littered around the coastlines of Britain and elsewhere. There were large quantities of surplus warships and merchant vessels to be towed for scrap or to destinations around the world for refitting and conversion.

Post-war disposals

The disposal of tugs built for use in the war years, or requisitioned, had important repercussions for the towage industry. Requisitioned vessels were in most cases returned to their original owners. Many tug owners were in urgent need of new vessels. Tugs returned from wartime service had often been worked hard for long periods, with little chance of proper refitting. The opportunity was therefore taken to purchase some of the many surplus vessels offered for sale by the various authorities. The majority of 'Empires' and 'TIDs' were sold off in this way. Where large numbers of vessels had accumulated overseas, such as India, Singapore, and Hong Kong, regional disposal organizations were set up. Lend/lease vessels were returned to the American authorities, who in turn sold a great many to commercial operators.

In this way a great many, relatively modern, tugs were made available for commercial use. Some tugs were still in shipyard hands when peace came. Of these some were scrapped but several were purchased by tug operators and completed to their specifications.

Of the larger oceangoing tugs, built for the British and American navies, the more sophisticated were either retained or temporarily chartered to commercial towage and salvage concerns. The 'Bustlers' were in great demand immediately after the war and several were chartered out. A few of these became quite famous. The *Foundation Josephine,* which features in the books of author Farley Mowat, and the *Turmoil* of the epic 'Flying Enterprise' saga, were both 'Bustler' class tugs on charter.

Many of the smaller wartime tugs were readily acceptable to commercial owners and great numbers were put to good use throughout the world. Temporary expedients have a way of becoming permanent! A very large number of the tugs, produced at great speed to fulfill the emergency requirements, were to remain in service for over forty years. Many are still in use. In years to come a high proportion of the former wartime tugs were to be extensively modernized. Steam tugs were often converted to diesel and in some cases the entire vessel was transformed to meet similar standards to newly built craft. This was only made possible by the high standards of construction inherent in the original vessel.

Post-war tug building

In some companies the need for suitable tugs that would be commercially viable was acute and could only be met by new construction. In Holland, where war had decimated the once efficient oceangoing tug fleets, building started almost at once. Although some former naval tugs were used as a temporary measure the opportunity was taken to re-equip with new vessels. By developing existing, proven designs large numbers of motor tugs were put into service very quickly. Most of the new seagoing tugs were single-screw vessels powered by one or two diesel engines. By the end of the 1950s leading major companies such as L. Smit had built up substantial fleets of 'advanced' tugs of between 1,000 and 4,500 bhp. In Dutch harbours the picture was much the same. Replacement ship-handling vessels were invariably small, economical diesel tugs, built in large numbers.

Oceaan *was one of several motor tugs built for the Dutch company L. Smit of Rotterdam as part of a post-war building programme. She was powered by Smit-MAN diesel engines driving a single screw with 2,000 bhp. This series of vessels, the construction of which started during the war, was part of a fast developing breed which was to dominate the world long range towing market.* Oceaan *is seen here with a dredger in tow. (Smit International)*

In Germany large numbers of tugs were lost to wartime action and as war reparations. Here, too, steam was largely forgotten in favour of diesel and diesel-electric power. Some of the technological developments, in their infancy before the war, were also beginning to bear fruit in more positive terms. It was in 1954 that the ship-handling tractor tug *Stier* was put into service in Bremerhaven, utilizing for the first time the unique Voith Schneider cycloidal propeller. This development and further progress with the Kort nozzle were to have considerable impact on the towing industry in later years.

Commercial tug fleets in the USA had not suffered losses at home in the same way as European companies. Building continued to replace older tugs in the normal way, without any notable changes in designs. As we have seen, diesel power was firmly established in the USA before the Second World War.

In Britain several well-known companies continued to build

steam-powered harbour and ship-handling tugs until almost the end of the 1950s. Vessels were built using designs that had evolved over many decades and incorporated the latest developments in steam machinery. They were oil fired and, as steam vessels went, economical to operate. The reasons for sticking so steadfastly to steam remained the same as mentioned earlier in this chapter. Diesel-powered tugs were being built, but the industry in Britain in the early 1950s was divided in its approach to propulsion systems.

Some cautious owners used proven steam tug hull designs and installed diesel propulsion systems. These were largely quite effective and many made use of the slow-running direct-reversing engine of the British Polar type. There was also a tendency to retain the traditional steam tug funnel—sustaining the popular myth that 'the bigger the funnel the more powerful the tug'. The new London tug *Vanquisher* was adver-- tised in 1955 as 'the most powerful tug on the Thames'. Owned by the Elliot Steam Towing Company Ltd, she was regarded as a very powerful ship-handling vessel but one retaining many traditional features. Her single British Polar main engine was rated at 1,250 bhp. *Vanquisher* was typical of many such vessels and gave good service until she was scrapped in 1982.

There were, however, new hull designs available and being used in harbour tugs of all types. The most popular of these was known as a 'Hydroconic' design. Tugs of this type were built in large numbers. The hull design was basically of a double chine form, produced largely from plates with little compound curvature requiring no complex rolling processes, as in normal ship-building practice. This design produced not only a cheaper hull but also one with good towing characteristics. The machinery installed was either single- or twin-screw diesel propulsion, usually incorporating gearboxes to enable more efficient, faster running engines to be used. In many cases no funnel was fitted, the engine exhaust gases being carried clear of the tug through uptakes incorporated in the mast or mounted separately aft of the wheelhouse. A Devon shipyard, P. K. Harris & Sons of Appledore, was responsible for a great many of these vessels. Large numbers of these tugs are still giving good service throughout the world.

During the 1950s most of the larger diesel harbour tugs entering service had engines rated in the order of 1,000-1,250 bhp. Direct control of the engines from the bridge was still rare in Britain. Engine-rooms generally remained fully manned, with one engineer on duty at all times to operate the engine controls.

The last of the paddlers

It is appropriate that mention should be made of the final

The introduction of the harbour tug Stier *in 1955 marked the start of a new phase of development in the towage industry. With her sisters, she was the first practical tractor tug to be put into service using the Voith Schneider cycloidal propellor. Her owners' successors, Hapag-Lloyd of Bremen, have continued to use the system and now employ some of the latest tugs of this type.* Stier, *powered by a 750 bhp diesel, is now in the German Maritime Museum in Bremerhaven.*
(L.O. Amboldt)

During the late 1950s a number of steam-powered harbour tugs were still being put into service with British fleets. North Rock *was one such vessel, built in 1956 for the Alexandra Towing Company Ltd of Liverpool. A vessel of 206 tons gross, she was an extremely efficient oil-fired steamer with a single main engine rated at 1,000 indicated horsepower. She remained in service until 1972, when she was sold to an Italian Company, as the* Capo Ferrato, *to serve for many more years.*
(Author)

demise of the paddle tug. A very small number of paddle tugs remained in service after the Second World War. A few stayed in service in Britain, owned mainly by harbour authorities or the Admiralty. The last paddle tugs in commercial service were withdrawn from use in northern ports during 1967–9.

There was one important attempt to retain the paddle tug concept. In 1956–8 the British Admiralty commissioned a series of seven paddle tugs powered by diesel-electric machinery. These unique vessels were built to berth aircraft carriers and similar very large warships. With their wide paddle boxes and lowering masts they could work safely alongside carriers, beneath the overhang of the flight deck. Two large electric motors were coupled to the paddles via a chain drive. Electric power was generated by four diesel generators. The power-plant was rated at 1,600 bhp. Using their paddles independently, the 'Dexterous' class tugs were extremely manoeuvrable and could produce a very powerful turning force when handling large ships. Most of the tugs remained in service until the early 1980s when they were replaced by tugs of the Voith Schneider tractor type.

1960-70: A very important decade

The early 1960s marked the start of a period of change in the towage industry that was to accelerate development in tugs and their propulsion systems at a rate far exceeding anything that had gone before. This period of change was brought about by massive changes in the parent shipping industry. Spectacular increases in the size of ships and radical changes in cargo handling methods altered drastically the demands made on towing concerns in almost every branch of the industry.

A new post-war 'Hydroconic' hull design proved very popular, particularly among harbour authorities. Diligent was built for the Dover Harbour Board in 1957, by P.K. Harris Ltd of Appledore. She was a 1,040 bhp tug of some 161 tons gross. Her hull-form can be clearly seen in this picture of her undergoing routine maintenance on the slip-way. She was sold by the harbour board in 1984 and was eventually acquired by Sorel Tugs in Canada in 1989 for further use. (Author)

Demands for more power

The development of oil tankers alone illustrates very well the changes that were taking place. In the immediate post-war years a tanker of 25,000 tons deadweight was dubbed a 'super tanker'. By 1960 this figure had increased threefold. The upward trend was to continue, until a couple of decades later a 300,000-ton ship was by no means uncommon. With ships increasing in size at that rate, massive demands were made on towage companies to provide suitable tugs to handle these unwieldy ships when they entered ports and oil terminals.

In the early 1960s the horsepower of new tugs intended for this work doubled. But this increase in engine power was not sufficient to produce the pulling power required by tanker owners, pilots, and insurers. 'Bollard pull', the static pull that a tug could exert on her towrope, was rapidly becoming the all-important criteria. In the past, a 1,000-bhp tug of traditional design was commonly producing a pull of some 10 tons. This was quite adequate for most ship-handling operations and experienced tug masters made good use of the weight of their vessels to hold a ship in position. It was at this stage that devices designed to increase the thrust of the tug's propeller became particularly important.

The Kort nozzle rapidly became the most popular means of gaining the necessary additional bollard pull. New standards for ship-handling tugs were set with 2,000 bhp and a bollard pull of 25 tons becoming common within a very few years. Little attempt was made to meet these standards using steam vessels, which could no longer compete in terms of efficiency or economy. Neither did the demands on tugs remain static—engine power and bollard pull were destined to double once more within twenty years—in tugs of this type. The quest for greater and greater efficiency in tanker handling tugs still continues to this day but with the emphasis aimed at com-

Grinder was one of seven unique diesel-electric paddle vessels. She entered service in 1958 with the British Admiralty. Her four main engines and two electric motors produced 1,600 bhp. This gave the tug a bollard pull of 16 tons and a free running speed of 13 knots. The paddles could be driven independently, giving her an enormous turning force. This picture illustrates her exceptional beam. She was 47.2 metres in length and 472 tons gross. (Author)

The American harbour tug Kerry Moran *is typical of many powerful diesel tugs built in 1963. She is a twin-screw shiphandling vessel of some 289 tons gross operated by the Moran Towing Corporation of New York. A diesel-electric propulsion system drives two open propellers with a total of 3,200 horsepower.* (J. Clarkson)

The tug Karet *was built in 1967 to handle tankers at the Shell International oil terminal in Willemstadt. Her diesel main engine of 2,250 bhp drove a single screw, rotating within a Kort nozzle. This arrangement gave her a bollard pull of 35 tons. She was purchased in 1982 by the British, Holyhead Towing Company Ltd for use in coastal and deep sea towing.* (Author)

bining power with improved manoeuvrability.

In time the demand for more powerful ship-handling tugs was to extend to ports handling other types of shipping. The massive increase in the size of tankers in particular also caused deep sea towage and salvage companies to look carefully at their ability to handle these giants, should they become disabled at sea or grounded on some coastline. Recent history has now shown how far reaching the effects of such an accident can be. Again the effect was a considerable increase in the size and power of the oceangoing tug. By 1970 very large tugs were entering service and trials were carried out with the current generation of ships in order to prove the

capability of the industry to deal adequately with such even-
tualities. In 1969 the German company Bugsier Reederei of
Hamburg put into service the *Oceanic*, a tug of some 13,200
bhp with an unprecedented bollard pull of 150 tons. For a
short time she was considered the most powerful tug in the
world but major advances continued and this accolade was
soon forgotten.

The industry faces wider changes

Changes in the oil trade were not the only significant factors
affecting towage. Shippers were also turning to containerization for most general cargoes. In the deep sea trades this considerably reduced the numbers of ships in operation. Those
that were to remain on the long haul routes become very much
larger than the previous generations of general cargo ships.
Special, larger, ships were also being introduced for bulk cargoes such as grain, ore, and coal. All of these made demands
on tug owners for more powerful vessels but there were other
considerations that were to affect the composition of tug fleets
in most major ports.

Improvements in the design of ships themselves was to
have a far-reaching effect on tug operators. Vast improvements were being made in the handling characteristics of
many new ships, particularly the smaller and medium-size
vessels. The installation of bow thrusters and other handling
devices succeeded in removing the need for tug assistance
altogether from a wide range of vessels. Such changes in the
parent shipping industry were eventually to result in a dramatic reduction in the numbers of tugs employed in harbour

*When she was built in
1969 the* Oceanic *and
her sister* Arctic *were
heralded as the most
powerful oceangoing tugs
in the world. They are
twin-screw vessels of
2,047 tons gross and
87.48 metres in length,
owned by Bugsier
Reederei of Hamburg.
When new, their Deutz
main engines were rated
at 13,200 bhp, giving the
tugs a bollard pull of 150
tonnes. Since then sever-
al modifications have
been carried out to
engines and propellers to
improve this figure even
further. (Author)*

fleets. The tugs remaining were, in general, more powerful and economical to operate and demands for improved versatility were also gaining in importance.

It is perhaps worth mentioning that in Holland and other areas the approach to handling large ships in port was quite different. Harbour tugs remained small and fleets relatively large. Additional power required to assist larger ships was met by providing more tugs. This resulted in very large tankers or container ships being attended by large numbers of small tugs. As many as eight or ten tugs could be found assisting one very large tanker. In time the economics of owning and maintaining large numbers of vessels and the consequent crew costs defeated this approach to harbour towage.

Changes in shipping methods also had a dramatic effect on the use of tugs and barges to transport general cargo on rivers and inland waterways. In London a thriving lighterage industry, which served the whole Thames area and its adjacent tributaries, was decimated in a very short time once containerization of cargoes started. During the 1950s over 250 tugs and many hundreds of barges were employed to move cargoes between wharves and serve visiting ships. A decline started in the early 1960s that was to continue until only a handful of craft remained in use. The pattern was repeated elsewhere, but in Europe and the USA many operators concentrated on bulk cargoes and some adapted their craft to transport containers, thus providing new services.

The offshore oil industry

Increasing oil exploration and production activities offshore had important implications for the towage industry. This type of work had been in progress for some time in the Gulf of

The fleets of the Dutch harbour towage companies contained a great many small motor tugs of relatively low power. Spitsbergen was one such vessel, of 376 bhp, built in 1958 for the harbour tug fleet of P. Smit Junior of Rotterdam. When, in later years, larger tugs were brought into service, many of the smaller vessels were transferred to barge towing and other duties.

Rebecca Theriot *was one of several American tugs to operate in the North Sea in the early days of oil exploration in the 1960s. She was part of a large fleet of vessels operated in the area by US companies for a number of years. This tug was a fairly basic traditional twin-screw tug but in time more sophisticated vessels were brought in, properly equipped for the work.* (J. Clarkson)

Mexico and elsewhere but during the early 1960s operations extended rapidly to the North Sea, the Middle East, and Asia. The area of operations was to grow steadily into less accessible, much deeper waters. Equipment also grew in size and complexity, placing constant demands on towage facilities. Tugs were required to move and position drilling rigs and equipment barges, as well as carry out a host of other duties, including laying and retrieving the very large anchors used to secure the rigs and other floating plant.

Initially, the tugs used were conventional, coastal and deep sea vessels with sufficient power and suitable handling characteristics. Where necessary, modifications were made to enable the additional duties of anchor handling to be carried out. Competition for this work was fierce. In the very early days of North Sea exploration much of the work was carried out by American tugs. American companies had gained much experience in this type of work from previous employment in the Gulf of Mexico and later in the Arabian Gulf.

European firms put considerable effort into producing suitable purpose-built tugs as quickly as possible. By the end of the decade a mixed fleet of European and American tugs were

European tug owners reacted to the need for purpose-built tugs for North Sea operation with newly designed vessels such as the Wandelaar. *Built in 1971, she is an anchorhandling tug built for oil related work by the Belgian company, the Union Towage & Salvage Company of Antwerp. She is a twin-screw 2,000 bhp vessel fitted with the necessary gear for off-shore operation.* Wandelaar *remains in service as a ship-handling tug in the Belgian fleet.* (Author)

at work in the North Sea. The tugs employed were invariably twin screw and again engine power was gradually increasing. Larger drilling equipment and supporting plant led to demands for more bollard pull. By 1970 tugs of 3,000 to 5,000 bhp were commonplace with many fully equipped to handle anchors efficiently. Many of these were modern tugs employed by European firms.

In the early days of deep water exploration the functions of the anchor-handling tug and the oil rig supply ship were quite separate. This was to change rapidly. Later generations of oil rig supply ships were to develop into sophisticated multi-purpose vessels capable of providing a whole range of services to their clients. The main purpose was to keep the oil rig, pipe-laying barge and the like fully supplied with stores, fuel, water, cement, drill pipe, and all the other commodities needed for work to progress unhindered. The ability to tow and handle anchors was an obvious additional facility, destined to become an integral feature of most supply ships. In time, very powerful vessels of this type were to cause a marked reduction in the number of anchor handling tugs employed in the offshore industry.

Changes in the industry continue

Little more will be said here about the period from 1970 to the present day. In the remaining chapters the various technologies and developments that emerged in this period are covered in some detail. Likewise a great many of the tugs entering service during this time remain in use. In the major fleets the economic life of a modern tug is likely to be about twenty years, much less than earlier generations of steam tugs. At the end of this first ownership, however, vessels frequently pass to another owner in a different environment to serve for another lengthy period. For this reason the towage industry, world-wide, operates a very wide cross-section of vessels with many older tugs performing a useful service in less demanding circumstances.

Tug development has continued at a rapid rate due to continuing demands for greater efficiency, safety, and economy. Periods of economic difficulty have dictated stringent cost cutting exercises in all branches of shipping. As a supporting industry, towage has suffered accordingly. Tugs had to become more efficient. Sufficient power must now be accompanied by a suitable standard of manoeuvrability to enable the vessel to operate safely and perhaps carry out the work previously done by a number of tugs. Automation of engine-rooms and the installation of sophisticated deck equipment has reduced the size of crews considerably.

Owners pursue maximum utilization, from what is now a very expensive vessel to build. Tugs stationed in ports and at oil installations are often called upon to provide other services. The most common of these are fire fighting and anti-pollution duties. Since the early post-war period, when the increase in the size of oil tankers began in earnest, tugs have been called upon to fulfil this task. Increasing emphasis on

Ralph Cross *was a ship-handling tug constructed in 1974 for the Tees Towing Company Ltd of Middlesbrough. In most respects she was typical of many British vessels employed in the work. She was a single-screw tug of 244 tons gross, powered by a Ruston diesel engine of 2,640 bhp. A Kort nozzle gave her a bollard pull of 43 tons and good handling characteristics. Her service with the company finished in 1989 when she was sold to a Maltese firm as the* Grez.(Author)

The British oceangoing tug Lloydsman *was the flagship of the United Towing Company Ltd when she was introduced in 1971. A vessel of 2,041 tons gross and 16,000 indicated horse-power, she was powered by two Crossley-Pielstick main engines coupled to a single screw. Her pro-peller was part of a 'Towmaster' propulsion system, incorporating multiple rudders, giving her a bollard pull of 135 tons and a free running speed of 18 knots. Her career was a short one; she was sold to a Singapore owner in 1979 to become the* Salviscount *and scrapped in 1987. (Author)*

environmental matters has made fire fighting and pollution control an important feature of many towage contracts. Tug fleets in most parts of the world continue to shrink. This includes not only the harbour towage fleets but also those of deep sea operators.

Difficult times for the deep sea tug

The day of the dedicated salvage tug is numbered. Since the early 1970s when large tugs of this type were being produced in large numbers, operating conditions have deteriorated con-siderably. It is now rarely viable, in economic terms, to main-tain large salvage and rescue tugs on station awaiting the call from ships in trouble. Such large tugs must be kept fully uti-lized. To some extent this has been possible in the past due to a demand for powerful tugs to make long sea voyages with ships for scrap or move huge pieces of floating plant or equip-ment by barge. These demands too have decreased in recent years. A developing heavy lift industry has been responsible for a sizable reduction in towage operations of this kind. Special ships, capable of loading and transporting large unwieldy loads, including whole oil rigs and even small ships, have been able to compete effectively with towage. Lower insurance premiums and shorter passage times have given the heavy lift ship a significant advantage. This has put enormous pressure on tug owners to bid for a larger share of work in the offshore oil industry and similar operations. Offshore, the tug has had to compete not only with the specialist supply ship but against increasingly difficult operating conditions. These changes have resulted in many of the less versatile tugs disappearing from service. Some have been scrapped after very short operating lives.

Technological advances

New technological innovations, particularly in the propulsion field, have continued to appear. One of the latest systems to gain favour in the industry is the azimuthing propulsion unit. This type of steerable propeller unit was first used to good effect in Japan in the 1960s where it was embodied in new standard tug designs. With this system it is possible to combine a high bollard pull with much improved agility. The tugs were originally used extensively in the Far East and the philosophy was soon adopted by some Australian owners. In Europe the azimuthing propulsion unit is used in two ways, in place of conventional propellers or mounted forward of midships in tugs of the tractor type. In tractor tugs it rivals the Voith Schneider system, which has become very popular in many fleets. In the last five yearthe use of stern-mounted units has grown enormously and tugs so equipped are found in many of the major fleets of Britain and Europe. British companies invested cautiously in the newer propulsion systems but the industry now embodies a good cross-section of the available technology. In the USA the use of some advanced propulsion systems has been inhibited by import restrictions applying to equipment of foreign manufacture.

CHAPTER 2

Modern tug propulsion and steering systems

The most important feature and the heart of every tug is its propulsion system. The number of systems, and the variety of ways that they can be utilized, has given the present-day tug owner a greater choice than ever before. The propulsion systems used in modern tugs range from a single conventional screw propeller to highly sophisticated units developed to combine exceptional manoeuvrability with great pulling power. This chapter outlines the major systems in use throughout the world. Several of the propulsion systems described are applicable to more than one type of vessel. Hence the equipment mentioned is tied only loosely to specific vessels or types at this stage. In later chapters, where tug types are described, the uses of the various systems will be fully defined.

Conventional screw propeller systems

The well-established screw propeller remains the principal means of propulsion for the great majority of tugs of all types. In modern tugs the conventional screw propeller is invariably used in conjunction with a nozzle or embodied in a sophisticated steerable propulsion unit. The individual systems will be dealt with later in this chapter.

Many of the tug fleets around the world continue to operate vessels that rely on propellers located in the traditional position, under the vessel's stern, and without any form of nozzle or thrust augmenting device. Such an arrangement is often refered to as an 'open' propeller. These are usually found on older vessels, still continuing to give good service, or tugs which for operational reasons remain most suitable for the local conditions in which they work.

In all ships propeller design is a compromise, but in the tug there are a number of conflicting demands that make the designer's choice more difficult. For example, in a ship-handling tug there is a need to produce good towing characteristics at very slow speeds; at the same time the vessel must travel quickly between tasks, and indeed keep up with the ships she may be escorting. The basic factors to be considered are: propeller diameter, pitch and rotational speed, and power. The diameter will be governed by the hull design, operating draft, and the power to be absorbed from the powerplant. Pitch can be defined as the theoretical distance the propeller will travel in one complete rotation. There are inherent inefficiency factors affecting the propeller that are too complex to be addressed here. Propeller pitch is interrelated to diameter and speed of rotation and is frequently chosen as the most convenient variable when reaching a compromise between pulling power and speed.

In simple terms, for towing purposes a large propeller with a fine pitch and slow rotation produces the best results. A smaller, faster rotating, propeller with a coarser pitch would be chosen where the vessel's speed was a more important feature. In order to operate efficiently the propeller must, ideally, be deeply immersed and have a free passage for water from around the hull.

Propellers may have three, four, or even five blades depending on their application. The choice of materials also varies, with bronze alloy, stainless steel, and cast iron as the most popular. The number of propellers installed on a tug depends very much on the type of vessel and its draft. Two propellers are frequently used where one cannot efficiently absorb the

The Suncrest *seen on the slipway for maintenance is typical of many conventional tugs with 'open screws' still giving good service.* Suncrest *was built in 1961 and is now operated on the Thames by General Marine Services. Her main duties are coastal towing and civil engineering work. She has a Mirrlees diesel main engine of 1,360 bhp and a bollard pull of 16 tons.* (Author)

necessary power without adversely affecting the hull design and draft. A twin-screw arrangement may also be chosen when manoeuvrability is an important factor. Three or four propellers are often used where the vessel is designed for operation in very shallow waters. Powerful pusher tugs frequently employ multiple screw propulsion systems in order efficiently to utilize high power main engines and keep the vessel's draft to a minimum.

Another important factor that must be mentioned is the choice of rudder or rudders. With open screw propulsion systems a single conventional rudder is still most common. With manoeuvrability high on the tug designer's list of priorities, a great deal of development has gone into producing rudders of suitable size, area, shape, and cross-section. The pivot point of the rudder and its cross-sectional shape are chosen to provide the best possible steering characteristics when the vessel is moving forward or going astern. The ability of a tug to perform well in this situation is crucial, particularly in harbour tugs. Perhaps the most important aspect of a tug's steering system is its ability to act quickly and positively. To this end the actuating mechanism is faster and more powerful than in many other craft and gives greater angular movement.

Rudders may be supported at the bottom by a pintle (hinge pin) to give added strength. Rudders unsupported in this way are known as the 'spade' type. In many tug designs more than one rudder is fitted. Twin rudders are sometimes used to give a single-screw tug improved steering and are the norm in twin-screw vessels. The use of propulsion nozzles also influences rudder design, as will be seen later.

In North America, additional rudders, known as 'flanking rudders', are sometimes fitted ahead of the propeller(s) to improve handling. Such installations are also common where the vessel is employed in pushing operations on inland waterways. There are a number of patented rudder designs utilized in tugs. Some have unique cross-sectional shapes and others additional movable blades of various kinds. All are intended to improve the tug's turning circle and handling.

Controllable pitch propellers

The controllable pitch propeller has proved to be an effective means of overcoming much of the need for compromise in propeller design. With this type of propeller the pitch of the blades can be controlled while the vessel is underway, to suit the work in hand. This has the following advantages:

(a) Propeller pitch can be changed automatically by a system that matches pitch to engine revolutions, giving the most efficient setting for the power available.

(b) The propeller can be used to provide astern power without the need for a clutch or reverse gear in the gearbox.

(c) Very fine adjustments are possible, greatly enhancing manoeuvrability. This is particularly useful when working in close proximity to ships or in confined spaces.

The pitch actuating mechanism is generally hydraulically operated and controlled directly from the wheelhouse. The pitch and engine speed controls are frequently combined and operated by a single lever. A disadvantage of the controllable pitch propeller is its relatively high capital cost. In some working conditions it can also be vulnerable to damage and consequently expensive to repair. Controllable pitch propellers are frequently used in deep sea tugs with wide operating parameters and powerful harbour tugs equipped with Kort nozzles.

Kort nozzles

The Kort nozzle mentioned in Chapter One has been developed considerably since its inception and is now capable of producing even greater improvements in performance. To quantify the benefits of a nozzle exactly is not simple since each tug design has differing characteristics, but generally an improvement in bollard pull of between 30 and 40 per cent would be expected, when compared with an open propeller. The nozzle is basically a tube within which the propeller rotates. In cross-section the tube is tapered with an aerofoil shape on the interior. The effect of the nozzle is to cause a differential pressure between the outside and front inside surfaces, inducing additional forward thrust from the nozzle. This additional thrust is transmitted through the nozzle mountings to the vessel's hull.

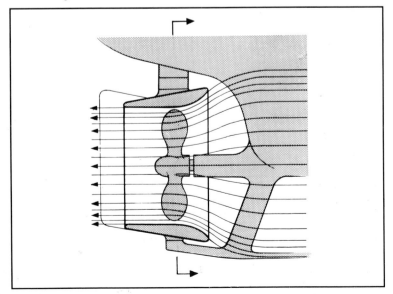

A diagram showing the flow of water through the Kort nozzle. The installation is typical of a single-screw steerable nozzle. Additional thrust generated by the action of the nozzle is shown by the arrows adjacent to the top and bottom pivot points. In a fixed nozzle thrust is transmitted directly through the structure.

Two forms of Kort nozzle are commonly in use: the fixed nozzle, which is part of the hull structure, and the steerable nozzle. The latter incorporates a rudder and is mounted on pintles in much the same way as a conventional rudder. When a steerable nozzle is used, the propeller shaft and its stern tube are extended to give the nozzle sufficient space to turn about the propeller, without fouling the hull. Such an arrangement is common in ship-handling and coastal tugs and is often used in twin- or multiple-screw propulsion systems. The steerable nozzle has the added advantage of providing a very good turning circle and general manoeuvrability.

The fixed Kort nozzle is one that encloses the propeller in the same way but is streamlined into the hull form. There is no rule governing the choice and tugs of many types use the fixed nozzle. It has the advantage of requiring a less powerful and less robust steering gear and is easier to incorporate in a shallow draft vessel. Certainly in very large and powerful deep sea tugs the fixed system is usually chosen. With the fixed Kort nozzle, single or multiple conventional rudders may be used, or special rudders designed to increase the vessel's turning circle.

The tug Sun London, *from the London fleet of the Alexandra Towing Company, is typical of many single-screw ship-handling tugs. She is fitted with a steerable Kort nozzle and Lips controllable pitch propeller.* Sun London *was built in 1977 for the Alexandra Towing Company Ltd. Her main engine is a Ruston diesel of 2,640 bhp, giving her a bollard pull of 45 tonnes.* (Author)

This twin-screw fixed Kort nozzle installation is the propulsion system of the Lady Theresa. Built for Humber Tugs Ltd of Hull in 1987, she has two controllable pitch propellers and twin patent 'Becker' rudders. A small ship-handling and general purpose tug, Lady Theresa has main engines producing 1,800 bhp (total). This propulsion system makes her very handy and gives her a bollard pull of 25 tonnes. (Author)

As with all modern propulsion systems, development of the Kort nozzle continues and various enhancements are available to suit particular vessels and conditions. One such enhancement is the 'Hannan Ring'. This is a particular Kort design incorporating a series of slots around the after end of the nozzle. The purpose of the slots is to improve the tug's handling characteristics when going astern. Propellers used in conjunction with the Kort nozzle can be of the fixed or controllable type, with the latter becoming increasingly popular. The blade profile of these propellers is specially chosen for operation inside a nozzle. In the illustrations, rectangular zinc blocks are in evidence, fixed to the nozzles and surrounding hull structure. These are to provide some protection against electrolytic erosion of propeller blades, nozzle, and hull plating caused by the use of dissimilar metals—ie a bronze propeller rotating in close proximity to a steel nozzle. The zinc blocks are known as anodes and work on a sacrificial principle.

The Kort nozzle is also used in conjunction with a number of other propulsion systems, of the azimuthing type, which are covered later in this chapter.

Towmaster systems

A system that showed great promise a decade or so ago but

that has not grown greatly in popularity is the 'Towmaster system'. Used on a variety of tug types, from harbour tugs to oceangoing vessels, the system is based on a fixed nozzle of a type not unlike the Kort design. The main difference is in the rudder system used. Rudders, described as shutter rudders, are positioned ahead and astern of the nozzle. Often three rudders are located astern of the nozzle and two (flanking rudders) ahead. The shutter rudders closely control the flow of water through the propeller and nozzle, improving both pulling performance and manoeuvrability. The Towmaster system has been used with a great deal of success to improve the performance of many existing tugs. A number of new tugs have been built with the system, including a series of successful ship-handling tugs for use in Australian waters.

The main engine

The term main engine is used in marine circles to differentiate between the engine used for the main propulsion system and engines installed to provide power for other purposes, ie power generation, pumping, and driving other auxiliary equipment. In modern tugs a diesel engine is invariably cho-

A typical 'Towmaster' nozzle and rudder system as fitted to an existing French vessel to improve her performance. In this installation the forward (flanking) rudders have not been included. (Burness Corlett)

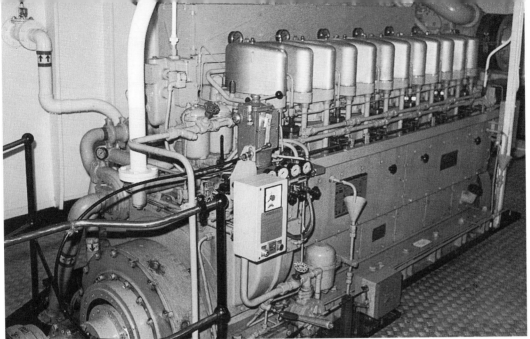

sen as the means of providing power for propulsion. There are, however, one or two parts of the world seriously considering reverting to steam. These are regions where the availability and low price of coal may lead to the steam tug being given a new lease of life. China is one such country.

Since the introduction of the diesel engine in tugs the approach to its use has changed considerably. The large slowly rotating diesel engines coupled directly to the propeller shaft are fast disappearing. A most noticeable feature of the modern tug's engine-room is the relatively small size of the engines. Not only are engines smaller, they are very much more powerful for their size. Engines have been developed to produce greater power by adding more cylinders and allowing them to run at much higher revolutions. This has been made possible by the use of modern designs, materials, and careful choice of cylinder configuration.

A typical modern diesel engine, used widely by the towage industry in Britain, is turbo-charged and has 6 cylinders arranged in line. It is commonly rated as producing in the order of 2,000-2,400 bhp at approximately 900 revolutions per minute. The rating of such engines may vary with the installation and the propulsion system—different maximum speeds giving different horsepower figures. Larger engines, producing much more power, may share common components with smaller engines from the same manufacturer's range. For example, a 12-cylinder engine, with its cylinders arranged in a vee formation, is likely to have many components in common with similar 6- or 8-cylinder engines.

Such commonality is practised throughout the world, as is the adoption of engines of a given type by various companies and fleets. By making use of engines of one type or from one manufacturer the purchase and holding of spare parts is sim-

The engine-room of the twin-engine tractor tug Hamtun *showing the relatively small size of one main engine. Two 6-cylinder Stork 6F 240 engines are fitted, each developing 1,350 bhp at 1,000 revs/minute. (Author)*

plified and becomes more economical. Engineering staff also become familiar with their charges and able to rectify problems more easily. For these reasons various engines become 'fashionable' in the industry—in later chapters it will be noticed that the same engines will be mentioned frequently.

The various horsepower figures quoted by towage companies often confuse the uninitiated. The output of modern diesel engines is usually expressed in brake horsepower or, increasingly, in kilowatts. Where possible brake horsepower (bhp) figures are used in this book. Brake horsepower is a figure derived from tests on the engine under load and in carefully controlled conditions. Indicated horsepower is sometimes quoted by operators in publicity material and was the normal means of rating the engines of steam tugs. This is a calculated figure which gives a rating approximately 13 per cent higher than brake horsepower.

The fuel consumed by the modern diesel engine varies in grade but is generally of the light or gas oil type. In large seagoing tugs much attention has been given recently to improving economy. Vessels of this type have been equipped to use cheaper, very much heavier, fuel oil which would normally only be used in larger ships and steam boilers. The equipment installed to enable this fuel to be used normally comprises special heaters and a filtration plant to lower the viscosity of the oil, so that it can be burnt by the diesel engine in the usual manner.

Engine installations and gearboxes

In order that the modern high-speed diesel engine can be used effectively it is necessary to provide a suitable means of transmitting the power to the propeller or propulsion unit, usually at a much lower rotational speed. There are various methods in use, including diesel-electric and hydraulic transmission systems; but by far the most common is the use of a gearbox. The engine installations described in this section refer to conventional propeller systems and do not include those used with more sophisticated propulsion systems, dealt with later in the chapter, where the engines may be mounted in a quite different way.

The use of diesel-electric propulsion systems was more popular in the early days of the diesel engine when it was more difficult to attain good control and power at slow speeds. A diesel-electric system is one where the main engine is coupled directly to a generator. The current produced powers an electric motor, which in turn drives the propeller shaft, giving precise control in a relatively simple manner. A number of engines may be used to generate power, for one or more propulsion motors. Such systems are, however, very costly to manufacture and no longer compete with the modern high speed diesel engine and gearbox installation in most towage applications. Many diesel-electric tugs remain in operation around the world, with the majority in American ports.

Diesel-hydraulic systems operate on a similar principle. The diesel engine drives a hydraulic pump and a hydraulic motor provides power at the propeller shaft. The connection between the two can be by pipes or hoses, giving greater choice in the location of engines, etc. These systems are expensive to manufacture and are generally unsuited to high-powered installations. Diesel-hydraulic propulsion systems are generally restricted to tugs of the launch tug and workboat type.

The gearbox is designed to transmit power from the engine to the propeller at a speed calculated to give the most efficient results. Generally, the gearbox has a fixed reduction ratio of somewhere between 3:1 and 7:1, thus lowering the output speed to the propeller by the same proportion. The gearbox may incorporate a reverse gear and automatically operated clutch. As previously mentioned, these are often unnecessary when controllable pitch propellers are used. In most installations the gearbox and clutch controls are operated hydraulically and interconnected to the engine speed controls. A brake may be incorporated in the gearbox or on the propeller shaft to control the movement of the propeller automatically when the vessel is manoeuvring. A high degree of automation is normal in the transmission system in order to protect the engine and gearbox from damage and simplify the controls in the wheelhouse.

In the most simple installation a single engine drives one

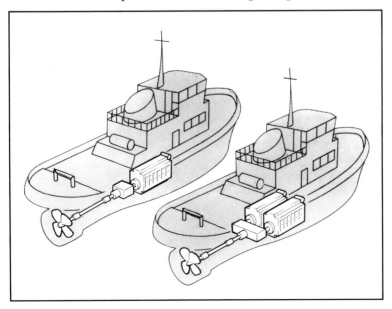

Typical installations of single and twin engines driving a single-screw propeller. The twin engine and single output gearbox arrangement shown is sometimes duplicated in a twin-screw tug employing four engines.

propeller through a gearbox. It is not uncommon, however, particularly in deep sea tugs, to couple two engines to one propeller shaft. This done by using a twin-input, single-output gearbox. The small size of modern diesel engines makes this a practical proposition and a four-engine installation, driving twin propellers, can provide an economical power-plant in a seagoing vessel. The advantages of such an arrangement are that an engine can be shut down for repair or maintenance while the tug is underway on a long voyage; or the vessel can proceed more economically on only two engines, while running light, without a tow.

Controls in conventional tugs

To complete this section on conventional tug propulsion systems mention must be made of the engine and steering controls. Engine controls have developed enormously over the past couple of decades. The days when the various engine controls were manipulated by an engineer in the engine-room and communication took place via the telegraph are all but gone in the modern tug fleet. One of the first major steps to be taken, once the diesel engine had become fully established, was to develop a direct link between the wheelhouse telegraph handle and the engine speed and reversing controls. This gave the tug captain a precise and predictable response while manoeuvring that did not rely on human fallibility or the need to build up a good working relationship with the man below. The introduction of the gearbox, combined possibly with the controllable pitch propeller, has simplified matters even further.

In most modern tugs the engineer is provided with a control station, often in a sound-proofed cubicle, from which he can operate and monitor all of the major items of machinery. Once the tug is ready to get underway the captain is given full control of the main engine and steering systems. In some small or highly automated vessels main engine starting may also be controlled from the wheelhouse along with some of the auxiliary machinery. Even in very large vessels, highly automated engine-rooms may be left unattended for long periods. Alarm systems are installed to warn of potentially serious or dangerous faults developing in the propulsion or auxiliary machinery.

In the wheelhouse the controls fitted vary considerably with the type of tug and specific preferences of the owners. For example, a single-screw ship-handling tug, with a controllable pitch propeller, may have a single lever to control engine speed and, within limits, propeller pitch. The combination of pitch and engine speed can often be adjusted in relation to each other by push-button switches or some similar means. To manoeuvre ahead or astern the pitch lever is used. Usually the

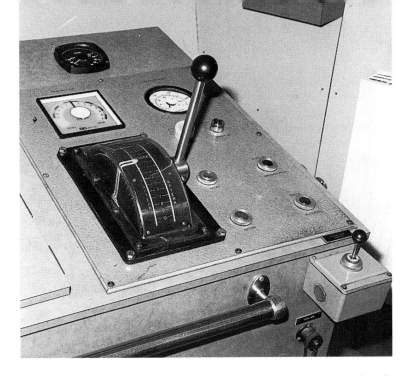

The combined engine speed and propeller pitch control lever in the single-screw tug Sun London *(see the earlier photograph on p.54 of her propeller and nozzle) is typical of many types in use. The white dials indicate engine revolutions and propeller pitch. Pushbuttons to the right of the lever enable the speed and pitch relationship to be adjusted. The small lever on the extreme right of the console is one of four steering control levers.* (Author)

lever is moved progressively forward, to move the tug ahead, and backwards to go astern. The same fine degree of control is possible in either direction.

A vessel of the same type would probably be steered either by a wheel, a small lever, or even a pair of push-buttons. Steering wheels are generally only fitted for emergency use in conventional tugs of any size. Small steering levers are common and a number may be installed, conveniently located to enable the vessel to be controlled from positions of good visibility. For the same reason, steering (and sometimes engine controls) are fitted to a small portable hand unit. The unit is connected by an electric cable to the control systems and enable the captain to position himself in full view of the work in hand—possibly outside the wheelhouse, on the upper deck. The permutations of possible control arrangements are considerable and further examples are given in later chapters.

Azimuthing propulsion units

The 'azimuthing propulsion unit' is an unwieldy but universal title given to a great many propulsion units of a similar type produced by a number of manufacturers. The terms 'rudder propeller' and 'Z drive unit' are also used. The trade names Aquamaster, Duckpeller, Z-Peller, Schottle, and Compass apply to units of the same type that are widely used in the towage industry.

An azimuthing propulsion unit is basically a conventional screw propeller that is driven through a system of gears in such a way that the entire propeller, and its shaft, can be rotated about a vertical axis—in much the same way as an outboard motor. Most units can be turned through a full 360 degrees, enabling thrust from the propeller to be used to propel and steer the vessel in any desired direction. The majority of units incorporate a Kort nozzle to improve thrust and have fixed pitch propellers. The unit's inherent gear train enables the propeller speed to be matched to the propeller and performance required with relative ease.

The propulsion unit is self contained. An upper gearbox casing bolts into the hull of the tug and contains not only the gears to drive the propeller but also the steering mechanism. A drive shaft connects the unit to the engine and the only other services required are electrical or hydraulic to control the steering gear.

Azimuthing propulsion units are used in tugs in a number of ways. There are two main configurations now frequently found in tugs, each invariably making use of a pair of units. Twin units may be located under the stern of the vessel in much the same position as the propellers on a conventional screw propeller tug. This is known as a 'stern drive' or 'reverse tractor' arrangement. To avoid confusion the latter term will not be used in this book. Alternatively, the twin units may be fitted beneath the forward part of the hull to provide 'tractor' propulsion. An azimuthing unit is also sometimes utilized as an additional bow thruster. When employed in this way the unit is generally fitted with a retracting mechanism to enable it to be housed within the hull when not in use.

Stern-drive installations

The early development of azimuthing units to replace conventional screw propellers in tugs of any size took place in Japan. In fact systems similar to those now rapidly finding favour in Europe have been in use in the Far East and Australasia for many years. The illustration (below) shows a typical stern-drive arrangement similar to many currently in operation

The tug Eldergarth *is shown at her launch in 1981. Twin azimuthing propulsion units are located beneath her stern. The tug was built for the Rea Towing Company Ltd of Liverpool and fitted with a Japanese Niigata 'Z Peller' propulsion system. Her main engines produce some 3,300 bhp giving her a bollard pull of 40 tonnes.* (Author)

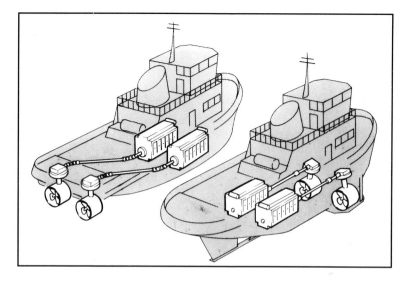

The two most common uses of the azimuthing propulsion unit in tugs. The units located in the bow of the vessel give the tractor configuration, requiring a vertical skeg in place of the traditional rudder. A stern-drive vessel has the units located at the stern in place of conventional propellers and rigid shafts.

throughout the world in tugs of between 1,000-5,000 bhp.

The azimuthing units are installed in strengthened mountings at the stern of the tug. Often the stern is higher than that of a conventional vessel. The actual mountings are frequently above the waterline giving the added bonus of enabling the units to be removed for repair without the need to put the tug into dry dock. A technical disadvantage is the need for complex shafting to transmit power to the units. The drive shafts are fitted with large flexible joints in order to accommodate the differing heights of engine and propulsion unit.

One of the main advantages of the system is that a very high bollard pull can be attained, coupled with impressive handling characteristics, yet without greatly increasing the draft of the vessel as many alternative systems do. Properly handled, the stern-drive tug can move ahead, astern or sideways and turn within its own length. To achieve these manoeuvres the units are turned, in unison or individually, to a whole range of positions designed to produce the correct thrust for the evolution required. The diagram shows the relative positions of the units for basic manoeuvres.

One of the most important features of the stern-drive tug of this type is that its bollard pull when towing astern is almost equal to that produced going ahead. This is of great significance in a ship-handling tug and a feature that cannot be reproduced in a conventional screw tug. In high-powered tugs of this type, the use of fixed pitch propellers can make very slow and precise control difficult—for example, when taking up the slack in a tow rope. To improve this feature of their performance a device is usually fitted in the drive system to enable the propellers to turn very slowly indeed. This takes the form of a fluid drive or slipping clutch arrangement,

63

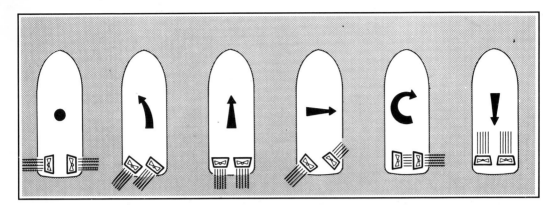

Above *The relative positions of the units required to accomplish the basic manoeuvres possible with the stern-drive tug. With the units located forward, as in a tractor tug, the same philosophy applies — with only minor changes in handling technique.*

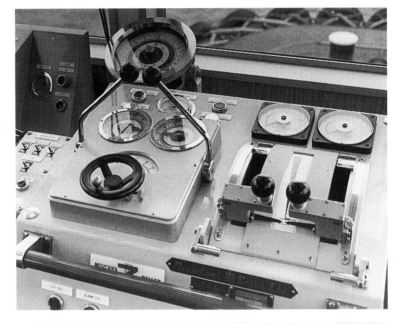

Middle *The controls of the Japanese-built tug Kenley represent one of a number of possible arrangements in use in stern-drive tugs. A small wheel steers the vessel with the units responding in unison. The levers above the wheel control the positions of the units, either individually or together, to enable the tug to move ahead, astern, or sideways. Two indicators below the levers show the position of the unit's nozzles. The large levers on the right control engine speed and the dials register engine revolutions. Kenley was built in 1985 for J.P. Knight Ltd of Rochester. (Author)*

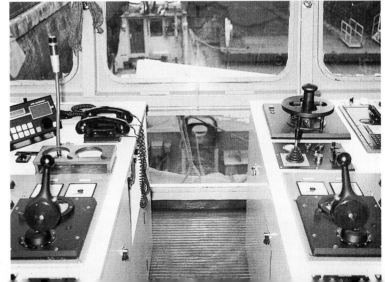

which is controlled automatically with the speed of the engine.

Controls in stern-drive tugs

Control of the azimuthing units in this type of vessel is quite complex and a number of steering systems have been devised to simplify matters for the tug captain. Electro-hydraulic systems are used to control the movement of each unit. In the wheelhouse, controls can vary from a complicated array of individual engine and steering controls for each unit to computer controlled single lever systems. Some operators and crews prefer separate individual controls, which appear daunting to the outsider. The engine controls and their speed indicators are straightforward enough, but there is no reverse position for the levers. In the azimuthing unit tug, 'going astern' is accomplished by turning the units through 180 degrees, thus directing the thrust forward. Each unit can be rotated using a separate lever. Indicators show the position of each unit in relation to the hull. With the units turned in unison, either ahead or astern, a small steering wheel is used to steer a course in the normal way.

When a single-lever control system is installed an electronic micro-processor controls all of the required functions. The lever is simply moved in the direction the tug is desired to travel. In some systems the engine speed control is separate; in others it is incorporated in the lever mechanism.

Tractor installations

Tractor tugs are very much a European phenomenon. Two types of propulsion system are used in the tractor, the Voith Schneider cycloidal propeller and the azimuthing propulsion unit. Both systems first found favour among tug owners in Germany but are now in use in many parts of the world. The azimuthing propulsion units used in tractor tugs are of the same basic design as those previously described in stern-drive tugs. Their location beneath the forward hull simplifies to some degree the installation of units and engines and reduces the need for complex shafting.

The handling characteristics of the tractor tug are, however, quite different. A deep skeg, or fin, is fitted beneath the stern of the vessel and the towing hook or winch is located much further aft than in conventional or azimuthing stern-drive tugs. In most designs no rudder is fitted but the skeg plays an important part in directional control during free running and towing. The manoeuvrability of the tractor tug is exceptional, with full control possible in all directions. The use of azimuthing propulsion units in tugs of the tractor type enables this feature to be coupled with a very good bollard pull performance.

Opposite bottom *The stern-drive tug* Brightwell *demonstrates a different approach to control systems. The vessel's 'Aquamaster' propulsion units can be controlled in two ways. A single lever control, located at the forward, right side, of the console can be used to control the movement and speed of the vessel entirely with one hand. Alternatively, each unit can be operated individually using the two large levers visible to the right and left of the console, further aft. Similar control systems are installed in many azimuthing tractor tugs.* (Author)

An often quoted disadvantage, however, is the inherent deep draft of the tractor, particularly when fitted with propulsion units of this type. A guard or plate is normally fitted beneath the propulsion unit propellers to afford some protection against damage if the vessel is run aground and to simplify drydocking.

Controls in tractor tugs with azimuthing units

Similar principles apply to the control of the azimuthing unit tractor as those previously described for the stern-drive type of vessel. The propulsion units are rotated to much the same positions, in relation to each other and the hull, to achieve similar movements. Controls in the wheelhouse also follow much the same basic pattern but the layout of the various levers and indicators may vary considerably from tug to tug.

Voith Schneider propulsion units

The present-day Voith Schneider propulsion unit is based on the unique cycloidal propeller invented by Ernst Schneider and J. M. Voith in 1928. The propeller is unlike any conventional screw propeller or paddle mechanism. In current practice, Voith Schneider propulsion units are invariably fitted in tugs of the tractor type. The tractor tug originally evolved hand in hand with the Voith Schneider system. As mentioned in Chapter One, most of the early development took place in Germany, but the Voith tractor tug soon became popular in many European ports. Acceptance of this type of propulsion has taken some time to spread elsewhere, but in the last decade or so examples have been built for use in ports all round the world. With the exception of very small tugs, most modern tractors are fitted with two propulsion units, side by side.

Each propulsion unit has a series of blades, pointing downwards, attached to a hub which rotates about a vertical axis. Each blade has a hydrofoil cross-section. At a predetermined position in the blades' circular path, a change of pitch occurs producing propulsive thrust. The action is not unlike the sculling action of an oar but uses circular motion rather than a more complex oscillating action. The circular path around which the blades travel is known as a cycloid— hence the name cycloidal propeller.

The point in the blades' path at which the change of pitch takes place is controlled by a mechanical linkage, comprising levers and cranks known as the 'kinematics', located inside the hub (or rotor) of the propeller. At the centre of the linkage is a control rod which determines the position where changes in blade pitch occur and the magnitude of that change. In this way thrust can be vectored in any chosen direction in relation

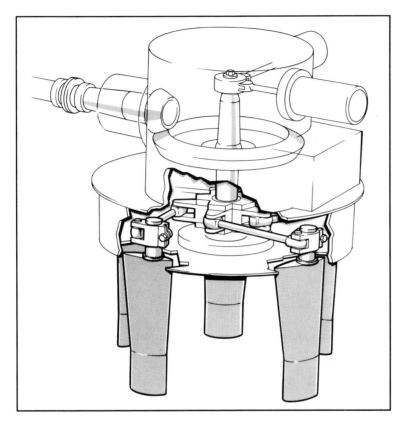

The Voith Schneider propulsion unit. This much simplified diagram shows the principal elements of the cycloidal propeller and its control mechanism. The cutaway section depicts the kinematic linkage which controls the pitch of each blade as the assembly rotates. In the centre is the control rod, connected at the top to its two servo actuators. The input shaft enters from the left and, through the bevel gearing, drives the entire rotor assembly.

to the hull and its force controlled with great precision. The diagram below shows a simplified blade arrangement and the way thrust is generated and directed. In practice, the number of blades used and the diameter of the blade path is chosen to match the power available and the size of vessel. The thrust available when going ahead or astern is almost identical and changes very little throughout the 360-degree steering circle. The Voith system affords a degree of control superior to most others, but in terms of propeller efficiency the cycloidal unit does not compare favourably with those based on the screw propeller.

Each propulsion unit is self-contained. The main casing embodies a mounting flange to secure the unit to the hull structure. The casing encloses the gear train to drive the hub of the propeller and the necessary lubrication system Located in the top of the casing is the hydraulic servo-mechanism used to operate the control rod. The wheelhouse controls are connected to this servo-mechanism, usually by means of a mechanical linkage.

The installation of the units and main engines is similar to that of the azimuthing tractor, with the engines low in the hull and a simple shaft drive to the units. The hull design also

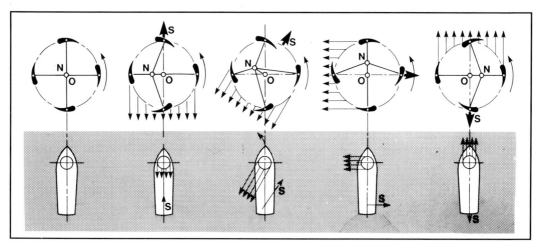

The effects of changes of pitch, in various positions in relation to the hull of the tug, and how they affect the direction of the thrust produced. The letter 'O' indicates the position of the control rod at the centre of the kinematic linkage. For simplicity only one propulsion unit is shown.

incorporates a large skeg at the stern and a protection plate is fitted below the propellers. This plate is often referred to as a 'nozzle plate'. It was discovered early in the development of the Voith tractor that the plate could be given a certain hydrodynamic cross-sectional shape and used to improve the flow of water and consequently thrust. The effect is similar to that of the nozzle surrounding a conventional screw propeller. In common with other tractor tug designs, the Voith Schneider-propelled vessel tends to have a relatively deep draft.

The operating characteristics of the propulsion units allow the main engines of a Voith tractor tug to run at a constant speed. Once the engines are started and the propellers are rotating, all further control can be carried out using the units' pitch controls. A useful by-product of having a constant engine speed is that auxiliary machinery can be driven directly from either engine. In fire-fighting tugs this is particularly advantageous, enabling high capacity fire pumps to be driven from the main engines yet leaving enough power available to manoeuvre the tug.

Controls in Voith Schneider tractor tugs

The controls of a Voith Schneider tractor tug are extremely simple and always take the same form. In the wheelhouse the captain is provided with a steering wheel and pitch levers. The number of pitch levers depends on whether the vessel has one or two propulsion units. One pitch lever is used to control each unit. These controls are located on a control stand and may be duplicated where necessary. Two control stands are often fitted in ship-handling tractors, one at the front and one at the rear of the wheelhouse, to give the tug captain a choice of operating position.

In very simple terms, the steering wheel controls transverse thrust and the pitch levers longitudinal thrust. The pitch levers have a central neutral position and as they are moved forward or backwards pitch is progressively increased in the ahead or astern direction respectively. Movement of the steering wheel introduces thrust to either side as required to steer the vessel. Small movements of the wheel produce changes in heading similar to any other steering systems, but as more wheel is applied increasing sideways thrust is produced. With the wheel turned to its full extent, in either direction, only sideways thrust is produced by the propulsion units. Transverse thrust always takes priority over longitudinal thrust.

The two pitch levers fitted in twin-unit tractors have a simple latch to enable the levers to be locked together and moved as one. With the latch disengaged the longitudinal pitch component produced by each unit may be controlled separately.

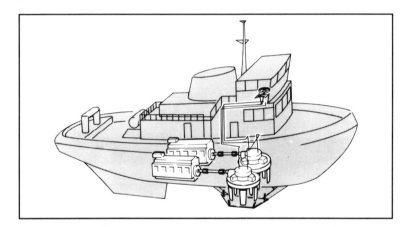

A diagramatic layout of a typical twin unit Voith Schneider tractor, showing the position of the propellers and engines. The control system has been added to show the relative simplicity of its mechanical linkage. Note the position of the skeg and nozzle plate.

This photograph shows the hull of the new tug Y816 in the process of being launched by crane. The blades of her two Voith Schneider propulsion units are clearly visible above the nozzle plate. (Voith Schneider)

One of three Voith control stands in the wheelhouse of the tractor tug Sun Anglia. *The levers on the right of the wheel control the propeller pitch. Note the catch enabling the levers to be moved in unison. Two small levers to the left of the stand control engine speed. The dial in front of the wheel is a compass repeater.* (Author)

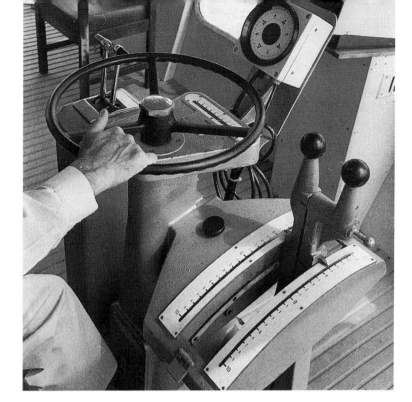

This gives extremely precise control when manoeuvring and enables the tug to turn in little more than its own length.

As mentioned previously, the units are designed to operate at a constant engine speed. In some installations, however, provision is made in the wheelhouse to control engine speed. This control may take the form of a speed control lever or a series of push buttons.

Bow thrusters

The term 'bow thruster' is a familiar one in shipping circles. Various forms of bow thruster are used in ships of all sizes as a means of improving their handling characteristics in port. In fact the installation of such units, in large numbers of medium-sized ships, has contributed greatly to a reduction in demand for ship-handling tugs. Bow thrusters are used in tugs for two reasons. A simple transverse thruster is often fitted in larger vessels to improve handling and station keeping in difficult conditions, whilst more complex, azimuthing, propulsion units may be fitted to ship-handling tugs to enhance their manoeuvrability and versatility.

Transverse thrusters

The most common form of transverse thruster found in tugs comprises a simple tube passing through the bow of the vessel. A conventional screw propeller is installed in the tube to provide thrust at 90 degrees to the vessel's centreline. The direction of thrust, to port or starboard, is controlled by changing the rotational direction of the propeller.

Power to drive the propeller is produced either by an electric motor, a hydraulic motor, or a diesel engine. In deep sea tugs the bow thruster may be quite a powerful unit driven by a powerplant of 400-600 bhp. Electric motors or hydraulic drives generally derive their power from auxiliary machinery in the engine-room. A diesel engine coupled directly to the thruster is also used but requires considerably more space in the normally cramped forecastle of the tug. In most vessels the bow thruster is controlled directly from the bridge.

The azimuthing thruster

The azimuthing thruster used in this application is identical in basic design to those used as main propulsion units. Thrusters of this type are generally fitted to existing screw-propeller tugs to extend their useful life or to fit them for a particular task. The term 'Combi-tug' is often used to describe a vessel converted in this way. The thruster unit is installed in the forward part of the hull, close to the bow. Most units are retractable and housed within the hull when not in use. This has the added advantage of enabling the vessel to return to her original draft when necessary, possibly to prevent damage in shallow water.

The vessel chosen for such a conversion is usually a single screw tug with a Kort nozzle of the fixed or steerable type. The thruster installed may be driven by a separate diesel engine, an electric or hydraulic motor. A powerplant of between 400 and 650 bhp is common. In a harbour tug space is at a premium in the forward part of the vessel and crew accommodation is often sacrificed to make room for the unit, its retracting mechanism, and powerplant.

The installation of an azimuthing thruster in the bow improves the handling qualities of the tug considerably. It enables the vessel to turn about its own axis and, when used in

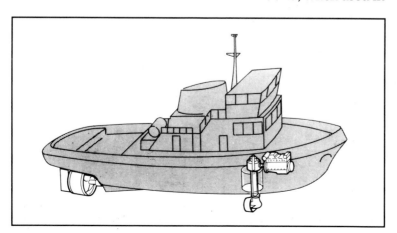

A conventional screw tug which has been modified by fitting a retractable azimuthing propulsion unit in her forward hull. When not in use the thruster is retracted into the hull. As the thruster retracts the drive mechanism is automatically disconnected from the engine. Such a vessel is often referred to as a 'Combi-tug'.

conjunction with the main propeller and nozzle, to move sideways. A powerful thruster also contributes a useful additional bollard pull of several tonnes.

Tug performance trials

Much has been said in previous pages about the performance of the propulsion and steering systems. It is perhaps useful to know how those aspects are measured. In newly built tugs, trials are carried out as a matter of course to establish that the owner's specification has indeed been satisfied. Such trials cover not only the performance of the propulsion and steering systems but many other aspects of the vessel and her equipment. The operation of deck machinery, fire-fighting installations, and life-saving equipment are among the many items to be tested. Trials are also carried out when major changes have been made to important items of propulsion machinery in existing vessels.

The most important propulsion machinery trials are those which establish the tug's ability to produce the required bollard pull and free running speed. In addition it is necessary to ensure that her handling characteristics are of a suitable standard for the work intended. Reliability is also confirmed by a lengthy sea trial or an endurance test of some kind.

Bollard pull trials

In these days of increasing demand for more powerful tugs the bollard pull rating of a vessel has become an important factor. Due to the variety of propulsion systems in use, and their different characteristics, it is no longer possible to judge the power of a tug by the horsepower of its engines alone. Therefore it has become necessary to devise a bollard pull test that can be universally accepted as the measure of a vessel's ability to tow. Bollard pull is simply the amount of static pull the vessel can exert when tethered to a measuring device. The figure obtained is usually expressed in tonnes.

To achieve accurate and meaningful results the trial must be conducted under carefully selected conditons, the most important factor being the location. The main requirement is for a large stretch of water unaffected by tides and of a suitable depth. Depth of water can be critical, especially in the case of powerful deep draft tugs, the performance of which is affected by a phenomenon known as 'ground effect'. A depth of water of at least three times the vessel's draft is desirable but not always easy to achieve. A suitable bollard is also essential. With modern harbour tugs producing bollard pull figures of 40-50 tonnes, it is not unknown for dockside bollards to be pulled bodily from their foundations during trials.

The tug's towline is shackled to the bollard with a measuring device inserted in the line. In many cases this will take the form of a very large spring balance, known as the 'clock'. More modern electronic devices are becoming increasingly common and have the advantage of being lighter and capable of producing a graphic record automatically. The towline length is also a critical factor. A length of some 150-200 metres is necessary to avoid water, thrust upon dock walls, causing false readings and control problems. With the tug pulling against the measuring device in this way, readings are taken at various predetermined power settings for set periods of time. From the readings obtained tables of results are compiled for

A rare view of a tug on trials. This photograph shows a bollard pull trial, with the tug tethered to a bollard and the 'clock', a very large spring balance, installed in the towline. Superintendents from the owners, Alexandra Towing, are overseeing the trial and noting the results. The trial was held to confirm the improved performance of the London tug Sun XXV following the fitting of a 'Towmaster' nozzle and rudders. Below is a close-up of the 'clock'. (Author)

73

The Voith Schneider trac-tor tug Seal Carr *being put through her paces shortly after her delivery. Trials are held to confirm many aspects of a tug's handling. Some are spec-tacular to watch!* Seal Carr *is operated by the Forth Ports Authority in Scotland. She is a twin unit tractor tug of 1,800 bhp. (Author)*

analysis. In most cases, particularly with ship-handling tugs, the trials will include the vessel pulling both ahead and astern, the astern pull being equally important in some applications.

Speed and handling trials

The free running speed of a tug is measured in the time-hon-oured fashion using the measured mile. A number of 'runs' over the measured distance are made, in each direction, to compensate for wind and tidal conditions. The results are a calculated average expressed in knots.

Trials to confirm the handling characteristics of a vessel will vary with the type of craft but in general tests will be made to measure the tug's turning circle, going ahead and astern, response to varying degrees of helm, and stopping distances from different speeds. All control systems have an inherent time delay. These response times are important, particularly in ship-handling vessels, and are the subject of scrutiny during trials. From the bystander's point of view the crash stop is the most spectacular trial. The vessel is brought to a stop from full speed by instantly going full astern.

CHAPTER 3

Towing gear and deck equipment

The towing gear and deck equipment fitted to a tug often determines how effective she will be in service. Vast power and impressive manoeuvrability can only be used to good effect if it can be applied to the tow in a safe and efficient manner. The vastly increased power available in modern tugs imposes greater demands on towing gear than ever before. As bollard pulls have increased, considerable thought has been applied to the towropes themselves and the gear required to handle them safely. Each new tug design or radical configuration has presented its own problems. In the present commercial climate the work must be done quickly, often with a much smaller crew. This has led to greater mechanization of towing gear and deck equipment generally.

The towing connection

In spite of its long history the towage industry has not successfully dispensed with the towrope as the primary means of connecting tug and tow. The types of ropes used and the gear to handle them has changed enormously but time-honoured principles remain in vogue. Alternative methods of establishing a towing connection have been tried but none have gained universal acceptance. Push towing may be considered the exception, but this specialized application is dealt with in a later chapter dedicated to pusher tugs.

In harbour tugs, attempts have been made to replace the towrope by articulated hydraulically-controlled arms fitted with huge suction pads. This method has been tried in Japan for ship-handling. The tug simply manoeuvres alongside the ship and attaches its suction pad on to the hull of the vessel. The articulated arm is then adjusted for length and position and the tug then tows or pushes as required. There are a number of drawbacks. The size of the suction pad required is of necessity very large, giving rise to problems of positioning on the ship's hull. Many of the most desirable positions for a tow-

This picture shows the after deck of a conventional screw ship-handling tug assisting a medium-sized cargo ship. The quick-release tow hook is visible and a man-made fibre towline. The leather covering of the rope eye and the sleeve on the rope are to provide protection against chafing on the hook and tow beam. (Author)

ing connection, at the bow or stern of the ship, cannot accept a suction pad due to the complex shape of the hull plating. There has been little interest shown in such a system in Europe or elsewhere.

The towrope

The terms towrope or towline are often applied to both fibre and steel wire ropes used for towing. The modern fibre towrope is a very different piece of equipment from that used in tugs fifty years ago. Before the introduction of synthetic textiles in rope production the towing industry relied on natural materials such as manila and hemp. Ropes made from these materials were heavy and very difficult to handle when wet. Once waterlogged they rapidly sank, presenting a hazard to the tug by possibly fouling her propeller. The size of rope required by a powerful tug of the day was enormous, often as large as a foot (300mm) in diameter.

Modern man-made fibre ropes have quite different characteristics and have become increasingly complex in their construction. The first synthetic material to be used in the towing industry was nylon. It had many advantages over the previous generation of materials but also several disadvantages. Nylon ropes stretch considerably in use and are extremely elastic. Both of these features make them difficult to use in many towage applications, particularly in ship-handling. The material still has special uses. In deep sea towing its elasticity is utilized—short lengths of large diameter nylon rope are connected into steel towlines to act as 'springs'.

Polypropylene and Dacron are among the more commonly used basic materials now used for towrope manufacture. The construction of modern towropes varies considerably and new approaches continue to appear as demands are made for stronger ropes that remain small enough to be handled. It is not unusual for the ropes used in powerful ship-handling tugs to be subjected to loads well in excess of 60 tonnes. Many ropes are not spun in the traditional manner but incorporate various methods of plaiting and multiple plaiting. In some very recent products the internal strands of the rope are only slightly twisted and not plaited in any way. The strands are kept tightly secured by a woven sheath which maintains the shape of the rope and protects the load-bearing strands from external damage. All the modern generation of synthetic fibre towropes are buoyant and relatively easy to handle. They are impervious to most forms of contamination likely to be encountered on board tugs but still need to be used with care. In many types of rope considerable internal friction is generated under extreme loads, particularly where they pass through fairleads, around bollards, and in knots. The heat generated inside the ropes under these circumstances can cause the strands to melt and the rope to fail.

Steel wire towropes, or hawsers, have for very many years been used in offshore operations and in all types of long distance towing. This type of rope is also used in many harbour tugs where a towing winch is used. As in the past the ropes are manufactured from high grade, cold drawn steel wire, spun in the traditional manner. The main advances in the production of the modern steel wire rope are not only in the more sophisticated grades of steel used but also in the protective treatments applied. During manufacture, and in use, the ropes are treated with advanced synthetic lubricants designed to reduce internal friction and resist damage from the salt water.

Combinations of steel and fibre rope are often used in a single towline. In harbour tugs a short length of wire rope is frequently used at the outer end of the fibre towrope. This is known as the pendant and is used to resist the loads and chafing where the towline passes through the fairleads and around the bitts on board the tow. As previously mentioned, short lengths of fibre rope are also used in conjunction with steel towropes to provide a degree of elasticity.

Chain cable is rarely used as part of the actual towline due to the difficulty in handling this material and its weight. It is, however, often used as part of the towing connection, between the towline and tow. Chafing is the main enemy to all towlines, particularly at the point at which they are secured to the tow. In long distance towing a single length of chain cable or a 'Y'-shaped bridle is used to make the connection aboard a tow such as a ship or large barge. The weight of chain in the bridle also acts as a spring to reduce the effects of snatching or shock loading in bad weather.

Towing bollards

In many earlier tugs, particularly in Holland and the USA, the primary means of securing the towrope aboard the tug was by using towing bollards. These take the form of large 'H'-shaped bollards on which the rope is secured in a particular way. The method of 'turning the rope up' on the bollards varies from country to country and port to port. Where American towing methods are used, towing bollards will be fitted on the fore-deck and on the towing deck aft.

This method of securing the inboard end of a towrope is still used in many tugs, but with very high-powered vessels it is now impractical and unsafe. The modern synthetic fibre ropes previously mentioned do not lend themselves to this method of towing, without damage, if high bollard pulls are to be used. Towing bollards are, however, convenient and often incorporated in the fairlead of a towing winch as a secondary means of securing a rope end.

Towing hooks

A common method of securing the inboard end of a towrope is a towing hook. This method is universal in most British and European tugs, where a towing winch is not used. Even when the towline is normally handled by a winch, a hook is general-ly fitted to provide a secondary means of securing a rope. The main advantage of the tow hook is its ease of use and the abil-ity to release the tow instantly in an emergency.

There are many designs of quick-release tow hook. All mod-ern hooks are designed to enable the towline to be released

The towing bollards shown here are of typical Dutch configuration but are also used to support the mounting for a quick-release hook. This is the installation in use on the 820 bhp Southampton tug/workboat Wyepush, *built in Holland in 1989. (Author)*

easily and quickly if the tug is endangered by capsizing or any similar hazard. To release the towline, the hook is generally designed to open or swing down, letting the rope slip away. This mechanism must be capable of operating even under the extreme loads imposed on the towline when the tug is towing or being dragged at full power. In earlier designs the release mechanism was a simple one, normally activated manually by a large hammer wielded by a member of the crew. Present-day hooks are usually released by remote control, a much safer procedure. The release mechanism may be operated via a pneumatic or hydraulic system, or by a cable, with controls duplicated in the wheelhouse and on deck.

Many tugs, particularly conventional screw vessels, have their tow hook located on a righting arm. With this type of mounting the hook is fitted on a long radial arm, which is free to pivot on the centreline of the vessel but allows the hook to swing through an arc to either side. A semi-circular track is usually fitted to guide the righting arm and hook. This arrangement is a safety feature and designed to reduce the likelihood of the vessel being accidentally capsized when the towline is directly abeam of the tug.

Towing winches

Towing winches were first introduced in tugs to handle the very long towropes used in ocean towing. The towing gear was extremely heavy and there was a need to find a means of shortening and retrieving the towline quickly and safely. The basic purpose of the towing winch has changed very little but in present-day towing concerns its use is rather more com-

A typical quick-release tow hook, in the closed position. The righting arm and its radial track are shown in the left half of the picture. The wires, attached to a trigger at the top of the hook, allow the hook to be released remotely from the wheelhouse. (Author)

mon. Harbour tugs and many more smaller vessels are fitted with winches to ease the workload on board and allow the tug captain to control the towline remotely from the wheelhouse. The winches currently in use are of two main types, the traditional drum twin and the friction winch.

Drum winches

The drum winch is by far the most common type of winch used in the towage industry. It is basically a power-driven drum, or barrel, on which the towline is wound. This type of winch is produced in many sizes and with many variations, but the principle remains the same. In modern harbour and ship-handling tugs a typical towing winch is likely to be fitted with a single drum, driven by an electric or hydraulic motor. The forward and reverse controls of the winch and a powerful brake are normally located in the wheelhouse. The winch will be sufficiently powerful to retrieve the towline and, with the brake applied, can withstand a pull in excess of the tug's bollard pull. A ship-handling tug may not necessarily be equipped with a winch powerful enough to shorten the towline with the vessel at full power. The winch will handle either a steel wire towrope or one made of synthetic fibres.

Many tugs of the azimuthing stern-drive type are equipped with two single drum winches, one aft and one on the foredeck. The bow winch in such an installation will often incorporate a windlass to handle the vessel's anchors.

Drum winches fitted in tugs designed for coastal and deep sea towing will almost certainly be more powerful and have more than one drum. Two or even three drums, side by side on a single shaft, are common. The drums will contain either

This twin-drum towing winch is fitted to the Dutch seagoing tractor tug Sandettiebank. *The drum on the left has a man-made fibre tow rope, used for shiphandling and work at close quarters. The right drum contains a wire towline for long range towing at sea. Note the capstan drum on the left end of the winch and the auxiliary tow hook at deck level. (Author)*

identical towlines or towlines of different dimensions, to be used for different purposes. The winches installed in large deep sea tugs may also incorporate a device to limit and control the tension on the towline. When in use the winch will pay out or wind in automatically to compensate for abnormal shock loads but keep the towline at approximately the required length.

A winch, known as the 'waterfall' type, has two or more drums mounted in tandem, with each drum a little higher than its neighbour. Winches with two or three drums are used extensively in anchor-handling tugs. One drum of the winch will be designed to provide the necessary power, and accommodate a special wire rope, for handling the very large anchors used by oil drilling rigs and similar floating plant.

A limitation of the drum type of winch, particularly where very high bollard pulls are involved, is that the outer layers of rope on the drum tend to tighten excessively. This causes crushing and damage to the layers of rope near the centre of the drum.

Friction winches

The friction winch, sometimes known as a twin drum capstan winch, is a fairly recent innovation in the towage industry. It was originally introduced in very powerful deep sea tugs to replace the drum winch and as an improvement over the earlier drum type. The winch employs two grooved friction drums arranged parallel to each other (see diagram) and driven in unison. The steel wire towline passes around both drums about five times. A third drum, simply a large reel, acts as a storage drum for the inboard end of the rope. The storage drum applies a small load to the inboard end of the rope, keeping tension on the turns around the friction drums. In this

A forward towing winch of the drum type is common on azimuthing stern-drive tugs such as the Japanese-built Kenley. The winch drum contains one of the newer synthetic fibre ropes with a woven outer cover. The winch also incorporates a windlass to raise the anchors and a capstan drum head. (Author)

81

The type of friction drum winch often used in large deep sea tugs. The two grooved drums impart motion to the towline in much the same manner as a capstan. The lower storage drum is generally located well below decks and contains the bulk of what may well be a very long wire rope.

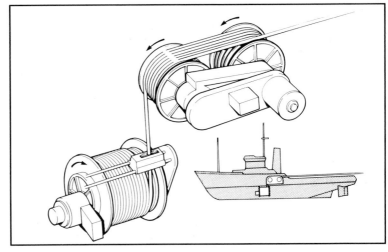

The friction drum winch, shown here on the Edengarth *of Cory Towage Ltd, is used with a fibre rope. The turns of rope can be seen on the grooved drums of the winch. A fairlead to guide the rope is located above a normal quick release hook. (Author)*

way the rope is wound in or out using the capstan principle, relying on the friction between the drum grooves and the rope.

There are a number of significant advantages in this system. Perhaps the most important is that there is no crushing or deformation of the rope. The winch in a large seagoing tug is generally located inside the superstructure. With the friction winch, the twin drums can be placed in the most practical position, from a towing point of view, and the storage drum located well below decks. This enables the great weight of the steel towlines to be kept low in the vessel, thus contributing to the tug's stability. A very large deep sea tug may have many hundreds of metres of towline onboard, including spare material.

The friction winch has also been successfully used to handle

synthetic fibre towropes. In Britain a number of ship-handling tugs have been built with winches of this type using exactly the same principle as those designed for steel wire towlines. In this application the winch is generally located at deck level with the storage drum in a convenient location adjacent to the engine room.

Deck equipment

Bitts and bollards
In common with all ships and smaller craft, tugs have an obvious need for the usual mooring bitts, or bollards. These are rather stronger in construction than in many other vessels because in some roles the tug is called upon to perform they may be used to help secure the tow. Many tugs are fitted with a large 'stem post' in the bow and similar 'shoulder posts' on her port and starboard quarters. These, likewise, have multiple uses in mooring and towing.

The capstan
Possibly one of the oldest pieces of mechanized deck equipment in the shipping industry, the capstan is still alive and well in many present-day tugs. The basic concept remains unchanged—a power-driven vertical barrel, with a concave outer surface, is used to heave and control ropes. The modern capstan is usually driven either by an electric or hydraulic motor and operated by a simple control, located conveniently near the user.

In tugs where no towing winch is fitted, the capstan is the most common means of retrieving or shortening a synthetic rope towline. Two or three turns of the rope around the capstan give the crew on deck assistance in getting the rope aboard easily and with a high degree of control. Where the rope is too large to pass conveniently around the capstan a lighter 'messenger' rope may be used to haul the towline on board in stages. The capstan is sometimes used in conjunction with a gog rope (see next section) to control the towline, as an aid during mooring and for many other purposes.

Many vessels have a drum head fitted to the anchor windlass or towing winch, which is used in the same way as a capstan. These horizontal drums are common in all types of tug and again have a wide range of uses. Many vessels, particularly in Europe, have separate powered drums located horizontally in convenient positions on the after superstructure.

Gog ropes and gear
Gog rope is a British term which refers to a rope used to control the movement of the main towline in ship-handling and deep sea tugs. The terms 'gob rope' and 'bridle' are also com-

The effect of the gog rope and two alternative methods of securing it. In the upper drawing a small winch is used giving complete control of the length and thus the effect of the gog rope. The lower view shows one of the many possible methods of securing a simple gog rope — using bitts on both sides of the tug.

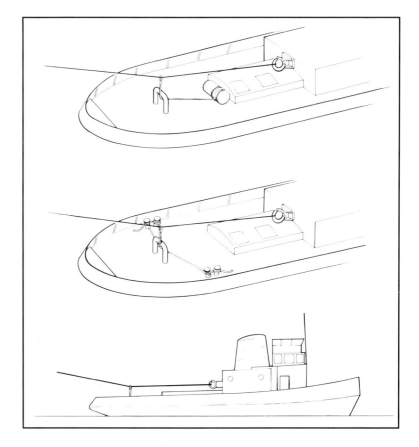

monly used in some localities for the same item. Bridle is also a name used to describe a 'Y'-shaped towing connection used between a towline and tow.

Conventional screw ship-handling tugs, working with a ship in difficult conditions, may use the gog rope to hold the towrope down, at a position close to her stern, thus effectively moving the towing connection aft. This procedure gives the tug captain better control of his tow and prevents the towline from being taken across the tug's beam, thus subjecting her to the danger of being capsized. Likewise, a deep sea tug may secure her tow in a similar manner also to prevent a long heavy towrope from getting over her beam to port or starboard. This precaution is usually unnecessary in American-style tugs, which have their towing connections located much further aft than their British or European counterparts.

Tugs using gog ropes are fitted with a large steel eye or fairlead on deck, in a position a little forward of the rudder post. The gog rope passes through this eye and is looped over the towline or attached by a free-running shackle. The inner end of the rope is controlled by a small winch fitted for the purpose, a capstan, or simply by securing it to bollards.

Tractor fairleads

In virtually all modern tractor tugs of any size, regardless of the type of propulsion system used, the towline passes through a large fairlead. The fairlead is a prominent feature of the tractor. It is precisely located close to the stern rail, above the underwater skeg. This has the effect of controlling the point from which the towline is effectively secured, in relation to the skeg, regardless of whether a winch or tow hook is used. A large tubular inverted 'U'-shaped structure is the most common form of fairlead, chosen to reduce the effects of chafing on the rope.

Tow beams

Tow beams are an item of equipment found less and less in modern tugs. This is the name given to the beams or guards used to prevent the towline from fouling or becoming entangled with items of equipment and fittings on the tug's after deck. These may take the form of guards located over individual parts of the vessel or beams which extend from bulwark to bulwark.

Stop pins

Stop pins, sometimes known as 'Norman pins' or 'molgoggers', are vertical pins that can be fitted in the tug's after bulwark rail, one on each quarter. They are often used in the conventional tug to prevent the towline passing over the side of the vessel, particularly when the rope is being retrieved and there is a danger of the rope end fouling the propeller. The pins take a number of forms, the most simple being solid or tubular pins inserted in sockets in the after rail. In larger ves-

This photograph of the tractor tug Sun Thames *shows clearly the large fairlead on her after deck and the effect that it has on the towrope when working at close quarters.* Sun Thames *is part of the London fleet of the Alexandra Towing Company.* (Author)

The after deck of the deep sea tug Kindeace *incorporates many of the features mentioned in this chapter. A Dutch-style towing bollard is used as a fairlead where the towlines emerge from her twin drum winch. On her after rail, the two hydraulically operated Norman pins are extended ready for use. Two full width tow beams are fitted to protect the fittings and capstan on the deck. A small crane is used to launch her boats or transfer gear. (Author)*

sels they may be supported in hinged brackets, allowing them to be erected when required. The very large, modern deep sea tug will have massive hydraulically-operated pins controlled remotely from the wheelhouse.

Fenders

One of the most distinctive features of most tugs, which always seems to impress the uninitiated, are the fenders. In spite of all the advances in tug technology, rubber tyres still appear in great numbers around the hulls of the vast majority of tugs. Very few vessels are required to work so frequently in such close proximity to other craft. However skilful the crews, preventing serious damage is a difficult problem.

A great deal of effort has gone into developing specially moulded rubber fendering to be fitted to tugs. Complex designs are carefully formulated to absorb the energy generated when two sizeable vessels repeatedly make contact with each other. This fendering not only has to protect the vessel from impact damage, which cannot be avoided in most towage operations, but must also survive the considerable abrasion encountered. Even in harbour, a ship-handling tug working in a swell, may range vertically against a ship by a metre or so. It is incredibly difficult to keep a fixed fender, in the form of a rubbing band, intact under those conditions.

Hence the popularity of the humble motor tyre. It is quite

common to see modern rubber fendering given the secondary protection of a layer of tyres. Discarded tyres from trucks and earthmoving vehicles have proved to be extremely effective in this role. They are cheap and easily replaced when totally destroyed.

With the exception of some of the largest deep sea vessels most tugs are required to push on occasions, with either bow or stern. Again, much effort has been put into providing suitable fendering and ensuring that the supporting hull structure is strengthened for the purpose. Among the novel designs developed to solve the problems of pushing against ships is a fully rotating fender constructed of heavy wheels complete with inflated tyres. A number of vessels are in use with the system but fenders consisting of various rubber sections are more commonly fitted to modern vessels.

Specialist deck equipment

Tugs employed in specialist duties, such as anchor handling for the offshore oil industry, are frequently fitted with sophisticated devices to enable their work to be carried out safely under extremely hazardous conditions. In these vessels the crews are faced with handling heavy anchors, their chains and massive wire rope pendants, in heavy weather and sometimes extremes of temperature. In order to assist with these tasks various patented devices have been developed to mechanize much of the work carried out on the exposed afterdeck of the

The tanker-handling tug Maria Luisa II was built with comprehensive rubber fendering to her bow. The fender is constructed of specially designed hollow rubber sections, bolted individually to her hull. Maria Luisa II is seen here being launched sideways by Cochrane Shipbuilders at Selby, Yorkshire, in 1988. She is owned by the British company Cory Towage Ltd and operated in Panama. (Cochrane Shipbuilders)

vessels. The more common consist of retractable 'jaws', 'stoppers', and clamping devices that can be raised from the deck to control the chains and wires used in anchor-handling operations. When not in use they are lowered, flush with the deck, but when in use are operated remotely along with the controls for the winches and other deck equipment. The use of this type of equipment will be mentioned in the section on anchor-handling tugs.

Deck cranes

In all but the largest tugs, the use of the derrick boom as a lifting aid on board tugs has practically ceased. The need for a lifting device remains, particularly in tugs involved in salvage or offshore work, where the movement of heavy equipment and spares can be an everyday chore. The derrick has been replaced largely by the much more convenient deck crane. Such cranes are usually operated electrically or hydraulically and range in power from about 2 to 20 tons lifting capacity.

The installation of small cranes has become very popular. Small hydraulic cranes, developed primarily for use in the road transport industry, have found a place on board many tugs. By using this type of equipment it has been possible to provide a useful crane on vessels of all types and sizes. The cranes generally have telescopic jibs and when not in use can be folded or stowed to minimize the space they occupy.

CHAPTER 4

Ancillary equipment

This chapter has been included to help familiarize the reader with many items of a tug's equipment that enable it to perform efficiently and provide the wide range of services now associated with this type of vessel. The term 'ancillary' does not mean that the items mentioned are unimportant. As with all forms of small ship, a wide range of equipment of all kinds is necessary to enable the vessel to operate safely and effectively with a crew that is economical in size. On board a tug even the more common items of marine equipment, found on almost any ship, are often of particular importance. Other, more specialized, features are fitted to improve the tug's versatility, and hence her ability to earn additional revenue for her owners.

The wheelhouse

The wheelhouse is the nerve centre of the modern tug. Unlike their predecessors, the captains of most present-day tugs rarely need to leave the wheelhouse to command their vessels from exposed open bridges. Remotely operated controls enable many functions to be performed by the master that would have formerly have been in the charge of crew members on deck or in the engine-room. As mentioned in previous chapters, controls for the engine, propulsion system, and much of the towing gear are located in the wheelhouse. Additional equipment is needed for the safe navigation of the tug and to enable her to communicate with other shipping, her owners, port authorities, and agents.

One of the most obvious features of the modern tug is the all-round vision possible from the wheelhouse. A great deal of thought has been given to this subject. By the nature of his job, the tug captain is often more concerned with what is happening astern of him than ahead, yet it has taken many years to achieve almost complete all round vision. Much of the improvement can be attributed to the discarding of funnels, or at least to adopting designs that make the least impact on visibility aft. Even now many owners are reluctant to dispense with vertical exhaust stacks—the alternative being engine exhaust outlets at deck level, usually in the stern rail.

Ergonomics, the study of efficient places of work, are increasingly being applied to the layout of controls and equipment in tug wheelhouses. This is particularly important in ship-handling tugs where a small crew is employed. The location of various pieces of equipment and controls can be a crucial factor, affecting both safety and efficiency. In relatively small vessels the captain may be seated in a swivel chair, in a position with good visibility, and with all of the essential controls grouped close at hand. In larger vessels, controls are duplicated at strategic positions. If the workload is high, the towing gear controls are manned by the first officer, or mate, leaving the captain free to navigate the tug.

Navigational equipment

The navigational equipment fitted in tugs depends very much on their employment. A compass is fitted in almost every type of tug. Magnetic compasses suffice in small locally based craft and instruments of increasing sophistication are installed in coastal and deep sea tugs. In seagoing vessels the equipment fitted differs little from a normal seagoing ship and in some cases may be superior. Gyro compasses are frequently connected to an 'auto-pilot' system even in the larger ship-handling vessels. This enables a course to be steered automatically, during passages at sea, once the vessel's directional heading has been set.

Radio direction finding equipment of various kinds is com-

The ultimate concept of 'all round vision' is demonstrated by the Tai Tam *of the Hong Kong Towage and Salvage Co Ltd. She is a 2,600 bhp stern-drive tug built in Kure, Japan, in 1987. Her central mast carries towing lights, a search-light, radio and radar antennae. The exhaust outlets for both main engines are located in her stern bulwarks. (Hong Kong T & S)*

mon in tugs involved in seagoing and coastal voyages. Systems such as the 'Decca Navigator' and 'Loran', which use signals from fixed coastal radio beacons, are extremely popular. Special charts are required to plot the incoming information and there is some restriction on the areas covered, but the results can be extremely accurate.

Many of these systems are being replaced or supplemented by modern satellite navigation equipment. This sophisticated electronic equipment uses signals from space satellites to provide accurate positional information, usually in the form of straightforward longitude and latitude figures. Advances in this type of technology continue to appear rapidly. The shipping industry is being offered new 'Global Positioning Systems' operating from chains of satellites. Such systems are based on work done by defence agencies and provide accurate, world-wide, navigational information at all times, unlike other systems which rely on certain satellites being in range for a few hours during each day. Doubtless the towage industry will eventually benefit when these systems become generally available.

Position finding is often a very important matter in towage. Accurate navigation for route planning is not the only consideration. In salvage and long-range towing it may be necessary to rendezvous with a casualty or another tug well away from coastal stations and local navigational aids. The offshore oil industry also requires great accuracy when positioning oil drilling rigs and other plant.

Echo sounder
In much the same way, accurate depth finding is also an important need in every tug. Because of the nature of their work, tugs probably spend more time in coastal waters than

The wheelhouse and superstructure of the ship-handling and sea-going tug Maasbank *illustrates the excellent view over the towing deck. Duplicate engine, steering, and winch controls are located by the large after windows. The exhaust uptakes support the mast, with its lights and two fire monitors.* Maasbank *is a stern-drive tug of 615 gross tons and 5,400 bhp, built for Smit International in 1987.* (Author)

The master of the tractor tug Hamtun *stands, or sits, between the consoles bearing the controls for the two Schottle azimuthing propulsion units. This is the view forward. A radar set is located ahead of the consoles. The microphones, on flexible stems, are activated by a foot-operated switch enabling the VHF radios to be used whilst leaving the hands free to control the vessel. (Author)*

most other vessels. They are often required to manoeuvre to assist ships aground. This demands an accurate knowledge of the depth of water and the profile of the sea or river bottom. Practically every tug is equipped with an echo sounder, an instrument that uses sound waves to measure the distance between the keel of the tug and the ground. This is a universal method of depth measurement used throughout the shipping industry. Modern equipment is available which can read depth to within a few centimetres. Tugs involved in salvage or inshore construction work are fitted with instruments which produce a recording of the depth measurements in the form of a chart.

Radar

Radar has many uses and has over the past forty years or so proved invaluable in tugs. Its most obvious use is in navigation in the dark and in poor weather conditions, particularly in coastal waters. In this role it is possible to locate accurately other vessels and various features of the shoreline. The modern radar set is a very advanced piece of equipment, compared with that of only twenty years ago. A typical modern radar, installed in a harbour or coastal tug, will have a high definition colour display screen and many features enabling range to be measured and possible hazards to be plotted automatically. In many sets the range will be adjustable between 3 and 30 nautical miles depending on the circumstances. Larger, seagoing tugs may well be fitted with two or even three separate radars. This enables, for example, one set to be used at short range—to monitor possible hazards nearby—and another to be adjusted to a longer range for navigational purposes.

In salvage work the radar set has transformed the whole business of locating ships in trouble. Used in conjunction with

modern navigational aids and communications equipment, searching is no longer the lengthy, tedious procedure it was in the early days before radar was invented. If a towline breaks in very bad weather conditions, providing there is no hazardous shoreline nearby, the tug may well make no attempt to reconnect until conditions improve. The tow will be monitored at a safe distance using radar and, if necessary, warnings broadcast to prevent collisions with other shipping.

Communications equipment

The subject of communications equipment, available to all types of shipping, is now a very broad one. Advancing communications technology has given the tug owner a wide choice of equipment and over the years has radically changed the manner in which a vessel can be operated.

Even the smallest tug is now equipped with a VHF (Very High Frequency) radio telephone to enable the vessel to communicate easily with her owners, port authorities, and other shipping. In most ports throughout the world the VHF radio telephone has replaced whistle signals and hooters as the main means of communication between tug captains, ship's masters, and pilots during ship-handling operations. The use of synthesized electronic channel selection circuitry has made such radio equipment extremely versatile. A very small radio set will often be capable of operating on all 80 channels in the international VHF marine band. This frequency band is intended for relatively short range use. Depending on the equipment and local geography conditions, 20 to 30 miles is normally regarded as the maximum range. Radios of this kind are standard equipment on all larger tugs for 'ship to ship' and 'ship to shore' use. Very often two or more sets are fitted to enable several functions to be carried out at the same time. A

Many modern radar screens are designed to be used in daylight, without the need for a deep hood to exclude sunlight. The 'Furuno' radar set in the picture is installed in the small tug Wyepush and set to operate at 0.25-mile range. It shows the area surrounding the tug at her berth in Southampton. The outline of the river Itchen and nearby Itchen bridge are clearly defined. (Author)

93

common facility on this type of radio telephone is known as 'dual watch', which allows the international distress and calling channel, channel 16, to be monitored regardless of other activities.

For longer range use, standard HF (High Frequency) and MF (Medium Frequency) radios are used, operating in the international marine bands. Radio equipment of this type is fitted in most seagoing tugs and has for many years been the standard method of communication between ships, owners, and agents, often working through the national coastal radio stations. The HF band also has designated distress frequencies. These are monitored not only by the various rescue authorities and shipping in general but also by towage and salvage concerns.

Satellite radio communications systems are rapidly growing in popularity. The dome-shaped antenna associated with this equipment is now seen on an increasing number of sea-going tugs. The main advantage offered by radio systems of this kind is the world-wide coverage possible, via the satellite link, without the need for complicated relay arrangements. This is of particular value when the tug is operating in remote parts of the world, away from established HF services.

The use of facsimile transmission in business has spread quickly among several branches of the shipping industry, including towage. Telex over radio was heralded as a great advance a few years ago. But this has been overtaken to a large degree by facsimile transmission equipment capable of conveying a wide range of documents. The possibilities this presents to the towage and salvage operator are immense. Charts, weather maps, technical information, and drawings are now transmitted directly from owners and agents offices to tugs at sea conducting towage, salvage, or offshore operations.

The deep sea tug Seaman, *owned by Humber Tugs Ltd of Immingham, displays a host of antennae on her wheelhouse and mast. Two radar scanners are visible and a number of vertical 'whip' radio aerials. The large white dome contains the satellite communications antenna. Her extensive accommodation is all above main deck level and her wheelhouse almost amidships. (Cochrane Shipbuilders)*

There is one other piece of communications equipment that has had a surprising impact among towage companies. This is the land-based cellular mobile telephone. Although its use is obviously restricted to the more civilized and densely populated areas of the world, this type of telephone now appears in the wheelhouses of many tugs of all types. Owners are finding such systems a convenient and relatively secure means of communicating with vessels in coastal waters. Business can be conducted in conditions of some privacy without broadcasting on international frequencies or resorting to encryption.

Accommodation

No description of the modern tug would be complete without some mention of the accommodation provided for the officers and crew. The standard of accommodation provided is generally very high. Towage, by its very nature, is a potentially hazardous and often arduous occupation. This has been recognized by the marine authorities in most major countries. Periodic changes in regulations governing crew accommodation acknowledge the need for high standards of safety and comfort. In most new tugs, crew accommodation is now invariably located above the waterline and considerable effort and expense goes into soundproofing the living areas.

Obviously the type of accommodation installed varies considerably with the type of work in which the vessel is engaged. Many harbour tugs and smaller craft are only used during the working day or on a shift system. In this case the accommodation will include little provision for sleeping on board and comprise mainly of the bare necessities for messing and little more. Other harbours operate tug services requiring the crews to stay on board for duties ranging from 24 hours to several days. This necessitates full sleeping accommodation and provision for the storage and preparation of food. Additionally, showers or bathing facilities will be provided along with drying rooms for foul weather clothing.

Seagoing tugs will be fitted out in this way as a matter of course, with standards of accommodation varying with the size of vessel and the type of work. In most vessels separate cabins are provided for the captain, chief engineer, and other officers. Very large tugs will have separate cabins for most of the crew members and rarely do more than two men have to share. Such vessels will also have sufficient accommodation available for owner's staff, salvage specialists, divers, or running crew. The latter term refers to the additional personnel required to man ships or similar vessels in tow.

Air conditioning and heating systems have become an important feature of many recent tug designs. The need for air conditioning equipment in tugs built for use in tropical and

The British steam tug Sun XII had a very long career as a ship-handling tug in the River Thames. She was built for the famous 'Sun Tugs' fleet in 1919 and served the company until 1969. A single-screw vessel of 196 tons gross, she had a triple expansion steam engine rated at 750 indicated horsepower. (Author)

near tropical areas is obvious. Many vessels, however, are required to operate throughout the world, placing an additional demand on the operators to provide suitable environmental standards on board. In the past decade or so the problem has been exacerbated by the need to operate in the colder parts of the world. The movement of oil-related activity to the more northerly regions of the North Sea and Alaska has placed additional demands on towage concerns. Tugs have been used extensively to move oil rigs and equipment in these areas. This has imposed a need for comprehensive heating systems to enable vessels to operate effectively in these extremely cold climates.

Lights and shapes

In general, the lights required by maritime law for navigational purposes are the same for tugs as for other shipping. There are, however, special conditions and requirements which affect tugs when they are towing. As in general shipping there are also day marks, or shapes, which are displayed for the same purpose during daylight hours.

Towing lights and shapes

To the uninitiated, the mast of a tug seems to carry an overabundance of lights. The vertical array of lights fitted to the mast are a combination of towing and navigation lights. The towing lights are illuminated in a particular order to indicate to other shipping that the tug is towing and give some indication as the nature of the tow. The regulations governing lights are revised from time to time but the following basic rules applied at the time of writing:

(a) Tugs below 50 metres in length need only one masthead steaming light. Over that length two steaming lights must be carried, on separate masts, in the same way as a conventional ship.

TID 164 is one of the 182 steam tugs of her type built for service in the Second World War. This example is one of a very small number that still remain in working order with their steam machinery intact. TID 164 was built in 1945 and remained in naval service until 1975. She is in the care of the Medway Maritime Museum and can be seen underway several times each year. (Author)

(b) A tug with a tow of less than 200 metres in length, from the stern of the tug to the stern of the tow, must carry one additional white towing light at the forward mast, 2 metres below the steaming light. A tug with a tow of over 200 metres in length must show two additional towing lights.

(c) A tug with a tow must show a yellow towing light aft, above her stern light.

(d) Three other lights are fitted at the mast of most modern tugs. These are two red lights, arranged vertically, sepa-

When new in 1955 the diesel tug Vanquisher *was regarded as the most powerful vessel of her type in Britain. A single 8-cylinder British Polar direct reversing diesel engine was rated at 1,280 bhp. Her superstructure was one deck higher than previous vessels giving her a particularly imposing appearance.* Vanquisher *was a tug of 294 tons gross which remained in use until 1982. (Author)*

The true proportions of the Eldergarth are self evident in this picture taken immediately prior to launching. She is a stern-drive tug equipped with engines and propulsion units supplied by Niigata of Japan. Eldergarth was built in 1981 for Rea Towing Ltd of Liverpool. A vessel of 352 tons gross and 3,200 bhp, she has worked in her home port and on ship-handling towage contracts abroad. (Author)

Very small launch tugs handle barges in much the same way as a larger tug handles a ship. The little Leonie is typical of many such vessels which operate in the Thames and other ports around the world. In the picture she has a 250-ton barge in tow and is gently stopping its forward movement by using her stern. The 150-horsepower Leonie is owned by Braithwaite & Dean Lighterage Ltd. (Author)

Right *An increasing number of tugs perform a dual role, operating as powerful ship-handling tugs and also carrying out seagoing towage work. Formidable is one such vessel. A twin-screw tug of 405 tons gross and 3,520 bhp, she is seen here preparing to berth a container ship in the Thames at Tilbury. Another tug, also from the fleet of Alexandra Towing, is taking up station at the stern of the ship. (Author)*

Opposite *Tractor tugs are ideal vessels for fire-fighting duties. The ability to use their propulsion units to counteract the thrust from the fire monitors is invaluable. Seal Carr is one of a pair of identical tugs operated by the Forth Ports Authority. Her fire-fighting equipment is controlled from a special protected cabin located above the wheelhouse, at the base of her mast. (Author)*

Right *In common with many tugs from Norwegian companies, Bjorn Eskil is a colourful vessel. She was constructed in 1983 for Bjergningskompanier A/S of Trondheim as a powerful ship-handling and coastal tug. Her twin Normo diesel main engines produce a total of 3,520 bhp. A transverse bow thruster forms part of her very comprehensive array of equipment. (Author)*

TUGS AND TOWING

Two massive Russian oceangoing vessels of 25,000 horsepower are currently the largest tugs in the world. Named SB131 *and* SB135 *they have twin controllable pitch propellors, driven by four main engines. Fixed Kort nozzles are fitted and this propulsion system produces a bollard pull of some 250 tons and a free running speed of 18 knots. One of the vessels is pictured undergoing trials in an ice-covered sea.*
(Hollming Ltd, Finland)

Robust *is one of three similar oceangoing salvage and rescue tugs remaining in service with the British Navy's Royal Maritime Auxiliary Service (RMAS). She was built in 1972, a twin-screw tug of 4,500 bhp and 1,036 tons gross. In wartime such vessels are engaged in a wide range of escort, search and rescue, and salvage duties. Peacetime employment usually includes towing redundant warships for scrap, moving floating plant, and participating in various training programmes.* Robust *is seen here taking a floating drydock in tow. (Author)*

Above *This scene was photographed on the Mississippi and shows a typical medium-sized American pusher, the* Lagonda, *pushing a rock barge. Note her immaculate livery and extensive accommodation. In the background is a similar vessel pushing barges with cylindrical bulk cement containers on pontoon barges.* (David Preston)

The mast of the tug Hamtun *shows the basic mast lights carried by most ship-handling and coastal tugs. The three towing lights are located beneath the highest masthead lights. Below them are the three red-white-red lights, duplicated on either side of the mast to enable them to be seen from all directions. On the wheelhouse roof are the magnetic compass, a searchlight, and a small rigid life raft. (Author)*

rated by a white light. This is the international signal for 'vessels restricted in ability to manoeuvre' and is often used by a tug at sea with a tow. The lights must be visible from all round the vessel and on many tugs are mounted on brackets to separate them from the mast.

Tugs of the tractor or push/tow type, which are capable of operating equally well stern first, may have two sets of towing and navigation lights fitted. The second set is positioned for use when the vessel is operating stern first.

During daylight hours a black diamond shape is hoisted to the mast of a tug with a tow exceeding 200 metres in length. The red-white-red light signal, 'vessels restricted in ability to manoeuvre', is replaced in daylight by two black ball shapes separated by a black diamond.

Portable lights are usually provided aboard tugs, to be installed temporarily on vessels in tow which have no lights of their own. These may be powered by gas or electric batteries.

In some ports local by-laws require special signals to be displayed indicating when a tug is operating with a tow. These are usually flag signals or shapes which are hoisted on a small additional mast.

Searchlights

Powerful searchlights are an important part of the tug's equip-

Opposite *This shot of* Morania 4 *pushing a very large barge demonstrates perfectly the 'pushing in the notch' technique.* Morania 4 *is a tug of 3,900 bhp built in 1973. The barge is high in the water, in a 'light' condition, illustrating the necessity of a high-level wheelhouse. If weather conditions make pushing inadvisable the tug disengages from the notch in the barge and tows in the normal way. (David Preston)*

ment. Almost every type of tug will have one or more search-lights. They have many uses. During towing operations a searchlight is used to keep a visual check on the condition of the towline and the vessel in tow. It can also be useful to iden-tify any likely hazards located close at hand by radar. Searchlights and flood lighting are used extensively during salvage and offshore operations to enable work to proceed around the clock.

Boats and life-saving equipment

The type of boat carried aboard tugs has changed drastically in the past twenty years. Rigid, full-size lifeboats, once com-mon on tugs of most types, are now rarely seen aboard any-thing but the largest vessels. The vast improvements made in inflatable life-rafts and the durable, semi-rigid rubber boat have been responsible for sealing the fate of the conventional boat.

Life rafts and other aids

For life-saving purposes the inflatable life raft, stowed on deck in a sealed container, has proved to be highly convenient for a number of reasons. The space required for stowage is insignif-icant and if necessary the number of rafts provided can be increased without difficulty. Rigid boats carried on tugs engaged in ship-handling work were a particular nuisance. Such boats are difficult to stow without impairing the vision from the wheelhouse and are easily damaged when the tug is working close alongside a ship. The need for davits to launch a relatively heavy boat compounds the problems of space, vul-

Maria Luisa II *is a British ship-handling tug built in 1988 to work in Panama. She is a stern-drive tug of 376 gross tons, powered by twin Ruston diesel engines of 4,340 bhp. Her accommo-dation is fully air-condi-tioned. An inflatable boat is positioned aft of the bridge and life rafts on either side. In addition to the fire monitors, above the wheelhouse, hose con-nections from her fire main are situated at the after end of her forecastle deck.* (Author)

nerability, and visibility. Most owners, throughout the world, were quick to dispense with the rigid lifeboat once a suitable alternative evolved.

A single modern life raft can easily accommodate the entire crew of all but the very largest of tugs. The life raft container is usually stowed in a cradle incorporating a hydrostatic pressure sensing mechanism which will release it automatically should the tug sink. Among the other life-saving aids provided are traditional lifebuoys, distress flares, and marker floats.

Workboats

Boats are frequently needed for purposes other than life saving. In earlier days the rigid lifeboat often doubled as a workboat. It was used to collect stores, transfer personnel, put towlines aboard other vessels, and for numerous other purposes. More often than not those duties are now undertaken by inflatable rubber workboats, powered by outboard motors. Such boats are durable, light to handle, and with suitable engines can be quite fast. The larger versions are regarded as semi-rigid, having a reinforced plastics lower hull and possibly an inboard engine. These types of boat are easy to stow and need only a simple hoist or crane to provide a means of launching and recovery.

Very large seagoing and salvage tugs are still equipped with rigid boats. These may take the form of lifeboats but generally they are intended to double as work boats and have powerful diesel engines.

Salvage equipment

Almost every tug carries some items that come under the heading salvage equipment. Even the smallest barge tug will probably have some additional pumping equipment on board

Salvageman is equipped for long-range towing, salvage and anchor-handling. Stowed aft of the superstructure is a workboat and fast semi-rigid craft, both within easy reach of a hydraulic deck crane. Fire monitors are mounted between her exhaust uptakes and searchlights on the wheelhouse roof. Due to her size she has a second mast to carry the requisite additional lights. Salvageman is a vessel of 1,598 tons gross and 11,280 bhp operated by United Towing Ltd of Hull. (Author)

to enable her to pump out or refloat flooded barges. The amount of equipment carried will again depend on the type of tug and her employment. Salvage is a very wide subject, on which much has been written; in the following paragraphs it is intended only to outline the basic equipment commonly carried aboard many tugs.

Salvage pumps

Additional pumping equipment is one of the most common facilities provided. This usually takes the form of high capacity pumps fitted to the tug's auxiliary machinery. The diesel-driven generators, air compressors, and other auxiliaries, located in the engine-room, often have provision for a salvage pump to be coupled to them when required. Such pumps are piped to connections, easily accessible, on deck to which suction hoses can be fitted. The purpose-built pumps fitted for salvage work are capable of moving water at an extremely high rate. Capacities of well in excess of 100 tonnes per hour are not uncommon. Tugs operating regularly in salvage work carry additional, portable pumps. These may be diesel-driven, self-contained units or submersible pumps driven by an electrical or air supply. Diesel pumps are stowed aboard the salvage tug and lifted onto the deck of a casualty if the need arises. Submersible pumps are designed to be lowered into the flooded areas of a casualty, connected to a hose. A common type of submersible pump popular on tugs is one driven by high pressure water. There are no electrical hazards involved and a suitable water supply is readily available on most vessels.

Air and electrical supplies

There is frequently a heavy demand on compressed air and electrical supplies during salvage operations. Again, the normal systems aboard many tugs are geared to some degree to provide external supplies of electricity and sometimes compressed air. The uses of electricity in salvage are easy to comprehend: lighting, portable tools, pumping, and welding equipment frequently require power from the parent tug.

The use of compressed air, to aid the refloating of badly damaged vessels, has been popular with the salvage experts for many years. Power tools increasingly use compressed air as a source of power, a much safer medium than electricity in a watery environment. There remain many steam-driven ships in use throughout the world. These often have a large amount of steam-driven equipment which is unusable if for some reason the boilers are out of action. Even simple actions, such as raising anchors, are then impossible. A service often rendered by steam tugs was to supply steam from their own boilers to such casualties. The only alternative most present-day tugs can provide is compressed air, which is quite effective in most circumstances.

It may be impractical to supply electricity or compressed air from the tug's own systems. Large seagoing salvage tugs carry onboard portable diesel powered generators and compressors. These are usually stowed in a salvage hold or in purpose-built lockers where they can be conveniently lifted out by a deck crane.

Anchors and ground tackle

Among the most common items found aboard a large seagoing or salvage tug are additional anchors. These are generally somewhat heavier than the vessel's own anchors and may well be of a special design. Additional anchors are used to assist with the refloating of vessels that have gone aground. They may be incorporated in ground tackle, very heavy multiple pulley systems rigged to exert a much greater pull than would be possible by towing alone.

Line-throwing equipment

Most tugs, of any size, have on board some means of getting a light heaving line to vessels that for some reason cannot be approached too closely. If a ship is aground in shallow water, or if the weather is exceptionally bad, the tug will not be able to manoeuvre alongside in the normal way. The most common method of making a towing connection under these circumstances is to fire a light line over the vessel by rocket or line-throwing gun. Once contact is made in this way heavier lines and eventually a towline can be hauled aboard the casualty and made fast. Line-throwing equipment varies from simple expendable rockets, which give one attempt, to guns that can be reloaded with fresh projectiles and line.

Underwater equipment

There is an obvious need aboard a salvage tug for some form of diving capability. In larger vessels this may be part of the tug's equipment, or alternatively provision may be made to accommodate specialist gear and personnel when required. The range of equipment carried can again vary enormously, from simple 'Scuba' diving gear to full scale deep diving outfits with a decompression chamber provided on board.

Included under this heading is equipment for cutting and welding and the means of carrying out other repair work underwater. Special tools are available for use underwater, such as spanners, drills, and hammers driven by compressed air. Some provision may also be made for the storage and use of explosives. The latter are used in salvage work for cutting purposes, to disperse wreckage and blast away rock.

Fire-fighting equipment

Fire-fighting equipment of some kind is installed on board every tug. This capability usually extends beyond that needed to protect the vessel herself from fires on board. The equipment fitted ranges from the provision of a few hose connections to sophisticated installations capable of undertaking important fire protection duties. Specialist fire-fighting tugs, their equipment and duties, are described in a later chapter. The following paragraphs deal with the more common and less specialized installations.

Fire mains and hoses

The term 'fire main' refers to a water supply, generally provided by a powerful pump in the engine-room, which can be used for fighting fires on board or on another vessel. A fire pump can be driven by one of the auxiliary engines or, in some tugs, by the main engine. The fire main is a system of pipes routed to deliver a supply of water to hose connections within the vessel and on deck. Hoses are attached to these connections and may be fitted with suitable nozzles for fire fighting. In most vessels the fire main is identified from the mass of other pipework by painting it red.

Monitors

Because of the difficulty in accurately directing high pressure jets of water during fire fighting operations, some form of nozzle is often used which is fixed to the structure of the vessel. These are known as monitors and have been mistaken by small boys for guns. In its simplest form the monitor is a nozzle located on a mounting designed to enable the water jet to be controlled with some accuracy. This is achieved by a system of handwheels and simple gear mechanisms. In the more sophisticated installations the monitor will be capable of delivering either water or a water/foam mixture. The output from a high performance fire monitor can vary from approximately 1,500 to as much as 60,000 litres of water per minute. If fire-fighting foam is used, the chemical compound needed is introduced into the water supply, prior to the monitor, from storage tanks installed on board. When foam is in use the volume delivered by the monitor is considerably higher than with water alone.

CHAPTER 5

Small river and harbour tugs

To try to put tug types into distinct categories is almost impossible. This chapter attempts to describe many of the smaller types of tug and the work that they do. A problem to ponder is, when do very small towing vessels actually rate as tugs? Many small boats, in use as workboats, passenger launches and even pilot cutters, have some provision for securing a towrope and when needed undertake small towing jobs. For the purposes of this chapter the starting point will be the small launch tug of about 20 gross tons and above. The other vessels in this first category are the wide range of small tugs which operate in harbours, rivers and inland waters carrying out a whole host of duties.

In many small commercial ports they are the veritable 'maids of all work', assisting small ships, working with barges and dredgers and involved in many of the routine maintenance tasks. A great many small tugs are employed by towage contractors specializing in supporting civil engineering work in harbours and riverside locations. It is common for such vessels to be owned by very small companies or owner-operators. These companies often work on a contract basis for individual jobs or are regularly hired to perform particular towage operations. Some make long coastal journeys to fulfil contracts in other ports. A great many small tugs currently operated in this way were formerly part of major tug company fleets and were sold off when they became too small, or outmoded.

An important feature of the very small tug is that it often lends itself to mass or series production. Using modern production methods, a number of companies build and market ranges of 'standard' tugs designed to meet a whole variety of applications.

Traditional barge tugs

Launch tugs
'Launch tug' or 'tosher' is a term used to describe very small

*The launch tug
Scoundrel is a tradition-
al River Thames 'tosher'
owned by the Thames &
Medway Towage
Company. She was built
in 1949, a vessel of 23
tons gross with a single
120 bhp National diesel
engine. She handles indi-
vidual barges in much
the same way as a larger
tug would with a ship.
The lifting platform is
rather unusual but is fitted to assist with bridge
inspection and similar
work. (Author)*

tugs of a traditional design used mainly to handle barges and
similar craft. Originally intended for use in the barge and
lighterage industries, many of these craft remain in service in
Britain and elsewhere. Few tugs of this type were built after
the mid 1960s but they remain popular due to their sturdy
construction, rounded hull form, and low profile. An average
launch tug will have a length of some 12-15 metres and gross
tonnage of about 20 tons. Most of the hull space will be taken
up by the engine-room. These are generally single screw vessels powered by a diesel engine of 125-400 bhp.

The launch tug was developed to handle barges singly or in
small numbers. They are used to marshall such craft in readiness for larger tugs and undertake the shorter journeys. To this
end the hull is strongly built to withstand hard use and the
low profile enables the craft to proceed under river and dock
bridges without the need for them to be raised or opened.
Barge companies still employ these vessels for their original
purpose but because of their ability to withstand hard use they
have proved very popular in the construction industry where
they are used to attend floating cranes, pile-driving craft, and
similar equipment.

The barge tug

Barge tugs of traditional design are still widely used on inland
waterways where barge trades have survived. Europe has a

large population of such craft operating in Holland, Belgium, and Germany, though many have been adapted to push their barges. In Britain very few have remained in their traditional trade but a great number have found alternative employment as small harbour tugs and contracting vessels. A 'barge tug' in the USA can mean a small craft, similar to those used in Europe, or a very much larger vessel used on major waterways or in coastal operations. In this chapter we shall deal only with the towing tug—in Europe and America, tugs of this type, size, and power are often equipped to push and tow. Examples of these are included in a later chapter on pusher tugs.

Like their smaller sisters, the launch tugs, barge tugs are invariably strongly built to withstand heavy contact with their charges. Their bulwarks are generally lower than normal, a feature which often identifies them from a harbour tug of the same size. The bulwarks are tailored to provide some protection yet be low enough to avoid fouling tow ropes or sustain undue damage from contact with barges. In size, most British and European barge tugs will be below 100 tons gross and 24.4 metres in overall length. They are fitted with a single conventional screw propeller. Twin screws are avoided by many owners because the propeller blades can be easily damaged by contact with barges.

The main engine will be a diesel of between 350 to 1,000 bhp. Their larger American cousins are often rather more powerful than this. In modern vessels a gearbox will be

The barge tug Jim Higgs *is seen towing a 'string' of barges specially constructed to transport refuse from the centre of London to riverside reclamation sites downstream. The tug was built in 1960 and rebuilt for her present role in 1985. She is a single-screw vessel of 109 tons gross powered by a 970 bhp Lister Blackstone engine.* Jim Higgs *is part of the tug fleet of Cleanaway Ltd. (Author)*

En Avant 31 is a Dutch barge tug, seen here with a craft in tow alongside. She is a vessel of 78 tons gross and 25 metres in length with a Caterpillar engine of 1,130 bhp. In common with many such vessels she has had several owners since being constructed in 1939. Her present owner is T. Muller BV of Dortrecht. (L.O. Amboldt)

installed but a number of direct reversing diesel engine installations are still in use. The engine and gearbox will be controlled from the wheelhouse and most engine-rooms capable of being left unattended for long periods. Kort nozzles are used by some owners and may be of the fixed or steerable type. Many older barge tugs have been fitted with nozzles to improve their performance—then a fixed nozzle is often favoured.

The methods used to handle barges depend on the type and size of barge and the conditions on the waterway concerned. On some waterways the total length of the tug and her tow are governed by local by-laws. Barges towed astern may be arranged in 'strings', two or three long and two or more abreast. On the River Thames, for example, a string of six barges of 250 tons each, three long and two abreast, was commonplace when the lighterage industry was thriving. Such tows still continue but the cargoes are mainly domestic rubbish for disposal or materials for building purposes. The tendency now is to use fewer but larger barges. When operating on tidal waterways, journeys are timed to make the maximum use of any advantage that can be gained from the flow of the tides.

In Europe and the USA barges are generally very much larger and used mainly for bulk cargoes. Single barges are often towed with the tug secured alongside. The tug is positioned very near to the stern of the barge. This arrangement enables the tug and barge to be controlled very much as one vessel and is particularly useful with light craft which sometimes tow badly astern.

The small standard tug

Small standard tug designs have become an important part of the current towage scene. A number of specialist builders offer designs ranging in size from very simple workboats to sophisticated anchor-handling tugs. It is the smaller type of vessel that attracts most attention and where the economic advantages of mass or series production can be best exploited. Tug builders in Holland have developed a considerable reputation for their small standard tugs, which are exported worldwide. Similar concerns exist in the USA, Canada, and the Far East. When ordering, owners choose the basic design that suits their purpose from the range offered, but some flexibility exists to specify particular engines or additional equipment. This arrangement offers the advantage of very quick delivery and much reduced design costs. With large numbers of similar craft in service the supply of spare parts is also simplified to some extent.

General purpose tugs and tug/workboats

A range of standard vessels has evolved in Holland to replace many older tugs employed by small harbour authorities, dredging concerns, and civil engineers. Although often referred to as tug/workboats they are regarded as true tugs by

The United States Army operates a large number of tugs in various parts of the world to support fleets of barges, cranes, and other vessels involved in military engineering. Tug ST2199 is a small motor tug of some 650 bhp used for that purpose. She represents one of several small standard tug designs used extensively by both the US Army and Navy. (Author)

Gray-Alpha *is a tug/workboat of a standard design from the Delta Shipyard in Sliedrecht, Holland. She was delivered to Felixarc Ltd of Felixstowe in 1984. The company operates several similar vessels to work with small ships and carry out general towage duties. The* Gray-Alpha *is a twin-screw vessel of 38 tons gross, powered by two General Motors main engines rated at 730 bhp (total), giving her a bollard pull of some 11 tons. (Author)*

the majority of owners. To many of the older tugmen they resemble large motor launches rather than true tugs, but their many advantages have made them a very popular product. Again, a number of sizes are available, normally from about 12-18 metres in length. For the uses mentioned a 15-metre version, of some 40 gross tons, is the most common. Most are twin screw and commonly powered by a pair of General Motors or Caterpillar diesel engines producing a total of about 750 bhp. Kort nozzles are fitted if required and generally a vessel of this type and size will produce a bollard pull of about 11 tons. A large wheelhouse is provided and sufficient accommodation for a crew of two or three. A small 'flying bridge' with duplicated engine and steering controls is sometimes fitted to give improved all-round vision.

Such vessels are extremely manoeuvrable and have sufficient power to carry out a very wide range of duties extremely economically. They are used in many smaller ports to assist ships and provide many other supporting services. The dredging industry was one of the first serious commercial users of these modern standard vessels. They have proved ideal tugs to handle the hopper barges used to take spoil away for dumping and to assist with repositioning dredging plant.

Where bigger and more powerful tugs are required suitable vessels are available from the ranges offered. In the small tug category a number of compact designs are employed, up to 1,000-1,200 bhp. In general these follow closely the designs used for larger ship-handling and coastal tugs but scaled down for a particular purpose. These are often employed as small ship-handling tugs or to carry out more specialized

GRAY-ALPHA

duties. Larger pieces of plant such as floating cranes are regularly attended by small twin-screw tugs that are powerful enough to attend them at sea if necessary.

Tractor tugs

There has proved to be a very real need for tugs of the tractor type in the small tug category. The ability to manoeuvre, with great precision, in any direction has obvious advantages, particularly when handling awkward craft in very confined spaces. Voith Schneider propulsion systems have been successfully applied to many quite small tractor tugs designed to carry out this type of operation. Several tug companies in Britain, Holland, Belgium, and France are using such vessels very successfully to handle small ships, barges, and floating construction plant.

A typical example is a type of small Voith Schneider tractor originally developed in 1964 to assist trawlers in the fish docks at Hull. Named Triton, Zephyr, and Neptune, the three commercial vessels proved extremely successful and were subsequently used as prototypes for a series of a dozen identical vessels built for the British Ministry of Defence (Navy). The tractors are only 18 metres in length. Each has a single propulsion unit driven by a 330-bhp diesel engine. They are used extensively in naval dockyards and at naval bases to work with the many barges and non-propelled craft used to service warships.

Tugs of this type are particularly useful in docking and undocking vessels at dry docks and slipways. The civil engi-

Taktow 1 is a twin-screw motor tug used to provide assistance to the giant floating cranes of the Dutch Smit-Tak fleet. She is shown here towing the Taklift 7 on a river passage, with her jib lowered onto a barge. Two other small tugs, the single-screw Agnes and the Voith tractor Triton, are being used to help control the forward barge. Taktow 1 was built by the Damen shipyard in 1981. She is a tug of 100 gross tonnes powered by two Caterpillar engines of 1,095 bhp (total). (Author)

The two smaller tractor tugs Agile *and* Adept *of the Alexandra Towing Company Ltd working in a heavy swell with the offshore barge* Kamosa. *This pair were built originally for a French company in 1971. Each is powered by a Voith Schneider propulsion unit driven by main engines of 580 bhp.* (Author)

neering industry sometimes has the need to position structures very accurately—for instance, components, piers, and lock gates. Small tractor tugs are frequently used in these operations. Secured alongside the lifting craft or supporting barges, they are able to use their directional thrust to control precisely the position of the vessels. In Europe tugs of a similar size are in use with twin propulsion units installed, considerably enhancing their agility and handling characteristics in difficult situations.

Tugs for special purposes

The duties of the harbour tug and barge towing vessel are perhaps obvious, but there are many more obscure forms of employment for the small tug.

Dredging tugs

In design and construction the dredging tug is little different to any other small harbour tug. In the industry today conventional screw tugs of the barge type or small standard tugs are often used. Such tugs are employed by port authorities, dredging companies, and companies specializing in providing tugs for this type of supporting activity. The tugs may carry out any of the following duties: towing non-propelled (dumb) hopper barges, moving and attending dredgers, surveying and raking.

The towing methods used are not in any way unusual. Hopper barges vary in size considerably, as does the journey to the dumping ground. Barges with a carrying capacity of 1,000 tons are common. In many instances the tug is required to make long voyages towing loaded craft out to sea to be discharged. On other occasions the journey may be to a pumping plant where the spoil will be pumped ashore for reclamation purposes. The tug may also be required to reposition the dredger, pumping plant, and floating pipelines. This often entails relaying the anchors used to keep the dredger in the correct position. Winches on board the dredger are used to control its position by hauling on the anchor cables. The tugs selected for a particular dredging operation are chosen with all these factors in mind.

Anchor handling for dredgers is little different in principle to the operations carried out at sea for much larger oil rigs. The smaller anchors used with dredging craft may weigh a tonne or so and the tug may be required to recover and relay them when necessary. In order to avoid fouling the tug's own propeller with the anchor cable, or recovery wire, the anchor may be hauled and secured near the tug's bow whilst running the anchor to a new position. A special davit and fendering is fitted to some dredging tugs for this purpose.

Accurate sounding and recording equipment is often installed in the tug to enable surveying to be carried out prior to, during, and after dredging operations. This work is important to ensure that the correct depths have been achieved and the required amount of spoil removed.

Raking

Raking, or ploughing, refers to an operation which was very common fifty years ago but fell into disuse in many areas. Originally, a tug was used to tow a specially constructed steel

Lord Waverley was built specifically for use as a dredging tug in 1960. She is a tug of 109 tons gross, powered by a single British Polar diesel engine of 935 bhp and operated by the Port of London Authority. Note the use of the gog rope, to protect the tug if she is overrun by her heavy mud barge. The strengthened area at her bow is where anchors can be secured whilst being repositioned for the dredger. (Author)

The little tug/workboat F49 is shown fully equipped for raking. Her rake is hoisted clear of the water whilst she moves between jobs. The 'A'-frame and the diesel-engined winch are designed to be easily removable when she is required for other work. (Author)

rake along riverside ships' berths, to remove silt and cargo spilt during loading and unloading operations. This ensured that, should a ship ground when the tide receded, no damage would be caused by debris lying on the riverbed. The process has become extremely popular in recent years, for a different reason. Tugs equipped with rakes are now used extensively to move unwanted silt and mud from adjacent berths and moorings. The spoil is moved away from shallow areas and jetties to enable a self-propelled suction dredger to manoeuvre and pick it up for dumping at sea. This is a much cheaper way of keeping berths cleared to the correct depth than employing more specialized dredgers. In order to carry out this work the tug requires a small winch on the after deck and some form of

Ala was purpose built in 1965 to work with trawlers. She is a vessel of 45 tons gross and 450 bhp. The wide rubbing band and inset super-structure allow her to work alongside trawlers without being damaged. Vertical guards are erected either side of her tow hook to prevent the towrope fouling fittings on her casing. She is operated at Lowestoft by Colne Fishing Ltd. (Author)

'A'-frame or fairlead at her after bulwarks to control the wires to the rake.

Fish dock tugs

In the early days of towage, the fishing industry made good use of tugs to assist sailing vessels into port. A small number of tugs are still employed by the industry throughout the world but in a quite different way. Once trawlers arrive in port after a lengthy voyage they are normally berthed to unload and the crews paid off. The vessel may then be required to move several times, to be repaired, refuelled, and prepared for the next trip. Without a crew, she is regarded a 'dead ship' and generally moved around the harbour by a tug. Tugs are still used when necessary to assist trawlers and other fishing vessels to berth or leave harbour, particularly if they are suffering some machinery defect. The tugs engaged in this work are generally small single-screw diesel vessels of about 300-500 bhp. Most of the towing is done with the tug fastened alongside her charge. This method requires no crew on the fishing vessel to steer or handle lines. A tug with a sturdy hull and good fendering is required. She must be a 'handy' vessel, sufficiently manoeuvrable to work in the frequently congested confines of a fish dock.

Small tugs for naval use

As we have seen in previous chapters, the navies of the world are well versed in building small tugs in large numbers and deriving the benefits of so doing. Small tugs are in great demand in dockyards and around naval bases to handle the

The British naval tug Georgina is swinging a small minesweeper through 360 degrees, around a buoy, to enable her compass to be adjusted. The tug is one of a series of identical, single-unit, Voith Schneider tractors used for handling small ships and barges. She was built in 1973 and is a vessel of 80 tons gross with a Lister Blackstone main engine of 610 bhp. (Author)

The Duke of Normandy, *seen here under construction, carries out a whole range of towage and maintenance work in the St Helier harbour in the Channel Islands. She is an 80-ton vessel built for the States of Jersey in 1972 by John Bolson of Poole. A single Caterpillar main engine is fitted. Her steerable Kort nozzle is clearly visible. The strange shaped bow and clear foredeck are designed for lifting and work on buoy moorings.* (Author)

smaller types of warship, barges, fuel lighters, and similar vessels. Many navies employ 'off the shelf' standard tugs with little modification. Others may develop their own designs in order to cope with special conditions and needs. They may have conventional a screw propulsion or employ systems giving superior manoeuvrability.

Buoy maintenance

In ports where one small tug is the only harbour craft, of any size and power and with perhaps a regular crew, she may have to perform a wide range of duties. A common task placed upon the harbour tug is the maintenance of marker buoys of various kinds in use around the port. This work will vary from routine maintenance, requiring only the servicing of lights and equipment in situ, to towing the complete buoy into port. In order to carry out this type of operation some means of lifting is needed to deal with the heavy 'sinker' or anchor keeping the buoy in place. A lifting sheave (pulley) in the bow or stern may be used or a small crane may be fitted. Larger harbour tugs carrying out this work may even take the entire buoy on to her after deck.

Logging tugs

In Canada, North America, Scandinavia, and other areas where forestry is a thriving industry, timber is still transported by water. Tugs are often involved in the process of getting tree trunks from riverside sites to sawmills using the waterways. Very small tugs are used to marshall these large logs at either end of the journey and in some cases assist in the construction

of rafts made up of large numbers of logs. The vessels engaged in this work are very small, sturdy, agile craft well protected against damage to hull and propeller.

The completed rafts of logs are in turn taken in tow to a sawmill for sorting and processing. A variety of tugs are used for the purpose, the main requirement being a suitably shallow draft to enable the tug to operate safely without fear of going aground on shallow banks and sand bars. Sufficient power and manoeuvrability are required to move and control the tow in what may be difficult tidal conditions.

Logging tugs come in many shapes and sizes. The Vitabjorn *is an elderly example employed in Sweden and shown here in the livery of Wiren's Rederi A/B (she has since changed owners). A vessel of 130 tons gross, she is a former steam tug built in 1899. Her present engine is a diesel of 560 bhp. Note the logs in the foreground chained together to form rafts. (L.O. Amboldt)*

CHAPTER 6

Ship-handling and coastal tugs

The Voith Schneider tractor Sun Anglia *was one of three tugs assisting the aircraft carrier HMS* Ark Royal *through the Thames flood barrier on a rare visit to London.* Sun Anglia *was built in 1985, a tug of 336 tons gross powered by two Ruston diesel engines of 3,444 bhp (total). She has a bollard pull of 38.5 tonnes and is fully equipped for fire fighting. (Author)*

Ship-handling tugs are probably the most important category of vessel as far as development and evolution are concerned. More effort is expended to develop tugs employed in the routine safe handling of ships than any other, and rightly so. A need for ship-handling tugs, in considerable numbers, will continue to exist in the foreseeable future. There are certain types of ship that will always require the assistance of tugs and, likewise, port areas that will remain accessible to ships only if towage can be provided.

Tug owners in the ship-handling business exist to provide these services but remain under constant pressure to do so at a reasonable cost, while facing increasing demands for power and performance. These pressures continue to have a profound effect on tug design and operation. Tug owners now have available to them a greater choice of propulsion systems and other technological advances than ever before to help

them meet these demands. This chapter attempts to show how that choice is being exercised and give some idea of what ship-handling entails. Coastal tugs have been included in the same category as ship-handling vessels because the two types are so often fully interchangeable.

Who are the owners?

It is difficult to indicate with any precision the patterns of ownership among the ship-handling fleets. This varies, as it always has, with the global location and the needs of the individual port. In the major ports of the western world the pattern is much the same. Large groups of companies, controlling tug fleets in several locations, have become commonplace. Such groups are established throughout Britain, Europe, Australasia, the United States of America, and the Far East. There are groups of companies operating fleets totalling 50-60 vessels in all of these locations. These fleets are usually split up and deployed in quite small numbers of anything from one to twenty tugs in various ports. In Britain, for example, two large groups provide towage services in a great many locations. The Alexandra Towing Company Ltd operates tug fleets in Liverpool, London, Swansea, Southampton, Felixstowe, Ramsgate, and Gibraltar. Cory Towage Ltd has similar arrangements in Bristol, Newport, Cardiff, Milford Haven, and Liverpool, with financial interests in a number of other tug fleets in Britain and overseas. This pattern is repeated with the Moran Towing Corporation in the USA, Progemar in France, Smit Tak in Holland, and a great many others world-wide.

Lady Sybil is one of three identical twin-screw tugs owned by Humber Tugs Ltd for use in Hull. They are compact vessels of only 23.9 metres in length and 160 tons gross but with twin Ruston diesel engines of 1,900 bhp (total). Fixed Kort nozzles and controllable pitch propellers are fitted and sophisticated Becker-type flap rudders. This arrangement gives good handling characteristics and a bollard pull of 25 tonnes. Lady Sybil is shown working as head tug on a cargo ship in Hull docks. (Author)

A useful by-product of group ownership is additional flexibility. Tugs of various types owned by the group can be transferred from one location to another to ensure that the most
suitable craft are available. In this way a higher proportion of
vessels can be kept fully utilized.

In the major ports there is often little opportunity for the
small independent operator in the ship-handling business.
Ports that once employed several tug companies are now rarely
serviced by more than one or two operators. The actual fleets in
use may be very small but contain relatively sophisticated
vessels. Where two major concerns have managed to survive
in the same location some form of work sharing arrangement
is often in use. The approach to towage by the major port
authorities is mixed; many prefer not to become involved with
providing towage services using their own resources.

In much smaller ports, what towage services are necessary
may be provided by the harbour authority, a small local operator, or by one of the larger groups. It is sometimes considered
economical to employ a tug from a neighbouring port, entail-
ing a short coastal passage.

Coastal towage is frequently a supplementary activity for
the tug owner whose principal business is the operation of
ship-handling tugs. It can provide useful additional revenue
and help to ensure tugs are fully utilized. To this end, many
fleets contain vessels suitably equipped to enable them to
carry out coastal and short sea voyages with ships, barges, or
contracting plant in tow. Such vessels are equally capable of
providing assistance to disabled ships in need of towage in
coastal areas. Tugs engaged in coastal work are also operated
by firms specializing in the work. As with the smaller tugs
mentioned earlier they are often former ship-handling vessels
that have become outmoded in their original employment.

This too is an activity that attracts the small owner or one-man business. Without the substantial overheads of the larger concerns, such firms may compete for a wide range of coastal towage jobs at very competitive rates.

The navies of the world still own substantial tug fleets, although these have been reduced considerably in recent years. Naval operators have also been subjected to cost-cutting exercises, resulting not only in smaller fleets but in rather more economical vessels. Many of the very large tugs, intended for both sea work and ship-handling, have disappeared. The British Navy and most European fleets now have very few large warships, of the aircraft carrier and capital ship types, thus reducing the amount of towage support required at naval bases. In the USA and USSR the situation is a little different, with large numbers of sizeable warships still in service. The type of work done at naval establishments involves ship-handling of the kind described later and some coastal operation.

Types of tug for ship-handling

The tugs used in ship-handling operations at present break down into three basic categories: conventional screw tugs, tractors, and stern-drive vessels. Claims are made expounding the advantages of each but distinct trends are emerging. It must be remembered that major factors governing the type of vessel include the operational environment and the service to be provided, as well as building, manning, and running costs.

Limitations placed on hull size and construction may apply

Antwerpen is a twin-screw ship-handling tug typical of many conventional screw vessels in service in Europe. She was built in 1983 for Union Towage & Salvage of Antwerp. A tug of 218 tons gross with main engines of 2,230 bhp, she is fitted with Kort nozzles giving her a bollard pull of 30 tonnes. Antwerpen is fitted with fire-fighting equipment and has a raised forecastle to improve her seagoing characteristics. (Union Towage & Salvage)

to all three types. The maximum size of many ship-handling vessels is governed by the size of a port's locks or entrances—it is often desirable for tugs to occupy the same lock as the ship being assisted or be small enough to pass along her side. These limitations may apply regardless of the tug type. A vessel operating in exposed locations, or involved in coastal and sea work, may have a hull with a raised forecastle to improve her sea-keeping qualities and help to keep the decks, where men have to work, free of water. A common requirement for ship-handling tugs is a good free running speed, to enable them to move quickly between tasks. In modern vessels figures of 12-14 knots are the norm, regardless of propulsion system.

Conventional screw tugs

Conventional screw tugs, with open screw propellers, Kort nozzles, and other thrust-augmenting devices, remain the most common type of vessel in service world-wide. But in some countries, this time-honoured means of propulsion is fast losing favour with tug owners.

In Britain and Europe alternative propulsion systems are being chosen for the vast majority of new vessels entering service. There remains, however, a large population of modern vessels, built since the early 1970s, with conventional screw propulsion. In most cases these are giving good service and many will remain in use for some time to come. The most up to date vary in size from 25-40 metres in length and 150-400 tons gross. They range in power from 1,000-3,500 bhp and the vast majority are of the single screw type. At the larger end of the scale they have bollard pulls of up to 50 tonnes and are used for work with large ships, or engaged in a high proportion of seagoing operations.

An important feature of any tug intended to work with ships is its ability to reposition itself quickly during the towing operation, in order to apply power in the required direction. In this respect the conventional screw tug is somewhat limited and can in fact be endangered by her charge. One of the most common hazards is the risk of being capsized by the towline if the ship makes an unscheduled movement when the tug has the towline over her beam whilst repositioning. This phenomenon is known as 'girting' or 'girding' and has been responsible for the loss of many tugs. Among the safety features used in modern tugs to minimize the risk are righting arms—on towhooks—and the use of gog ropes. These have been described in preceding chapters. It is, however, the matter of easy and safe repositioning that has given other designs an advantage over the conventional screw tug.

The real advantage of the deep draft, Kort nozzle tug is its ability to produce a high bollard pull at moderate power settings. By modern standards, its handling characteristics may be limited but quite adequate for the work that it does. Many tanker-handling tugs employed by major operators fall within this category. The prime need is for sufficient power to work with very large ships at riverside berths. Tugs of approximately 38 metres in length and about 3,000 bhp are typical of many in service at oil refineries and terminals in Britain, Europe, and elsewhere.

Similar, relatively large tugs, employed as part of a ship-handling fleet, are often equipped with suitable deck and navigational equipment to enable them to operate efficiently at sea. Towing winches, carrying towlines suitable for both harbour towage and sea work, on separate drums, are fitted to enable them to change roles with a minimum of additional preparation.

The USA is one country that has doggedly retained tug designs employing the conventional screw propeller, often with fixed and sometimes steerable Kort nozzles. The majority of modern tugs employed in ship-handling are twin-screw vessels. A common additional refinement is the installation of flanking rudders, fitted ahead of the propellers. The power ratings quoted for some of the most recent vessels are as high as 6,000 bhp. Tugs of the tractor or stern-drive type are comparatively rare.

Although comparable in size to their European counterparts, the American tug is often of heavier construction. The ship-handling methods used in the USA demand much more contact with the ship and thus more risk of damage. Towing bollards are still in use in most fleets, fitted on the foredeck and aft. Towing winches are installed aft on the more powerful

Deep draft single-screw tugs with Kort nozzles have proved to be very popular vessels for handling large ships. The Scottish tug Kelty is seen working with a tanker at the Hound Point oil terminal on the Firth of Forth. Owned by Forth Tugs Ltd, she was built in 1976. Her single controllable pitch propeller is driven by a Ruston main engine of 2,640 bhp, giving the tug a bollard pull of 35 tons. (Author)

Judy Moran is waiting to assist a passenger liner from her berth in New York. The tug has a tow-line connected to her forward bollards in readiness to tow away stern first. Her mast is folded down to enable her to work close alongside the ship without fear of damage. Judy Moran is a twin-screw tug of 275 tons gross and 3,300 bhp, built in 1973 for the Moran Towing Corporation. (L.O. Amboldt)

and versatile vessels. In the last few decades the towing gear on some types of American tug have been installed further forward than was common in the past. This is usually the case in vessels intended to work extensively with a towrope over the stern, rather than close alongside the tow.

The tugs used for ship-handling in many American ports are very much multi-purpose vessels. Barge towing is a duty that may well be part of the everyday work of the same tug fleet. Many of the barges are very large and the journeys, on rivers and coasts very long. The barges will be pushed or towed depending on the circumstances. Pushing barges is dealt with in a later chapter.

Tractor tugs

The tractor tug has become a very popular means of assisting ships, particularly in ports where there are enclosed docks or berths requiring intricate manoeuvres in difficult tidal conditions. The first tractors, introduced with the Voith Schneider propulsion system, brought a new dimension to the work. Their ability to apply thrust in any direction and handle equally well when going astern offered many new possibilities. Operating with the towline secured right aft, virtually eliminating the possibility of the tug being capsized by her tow, offered very safe operation. Many owners, however, while recognizing the handling advantages, found that this type of vessel did not produce the required bollard pull performance needed for their purposes. Although this restricted the use of many earlier tugs, some remain in service with port authorities, naval, and commercial operators.

The newer breeds of tractor have eradicated many of the earlier shortcomings and they are in use in most parts of the world. New ship-handling tractors, with the exception of very small craft, invariably incorporate twin propulsion units.

Voith Schneider tractor tugs of over 4,000 bhp are in service and bollard pulls of between 35-45 tonnes not unusual. For precise manoeuvring and relatively simple operation the system has much to recommend it.

Tractors incorporating azimuthing propulsion units first became popular in Germany, in the port of Hamburg. In 1972 Bugsier Reederei introduced a ship-handling tractor of this type, the *Bugsier 2*. Since that date the Bugsier fleet and many other companies have adopted the concept, which combines the higher bollard pulls possible with the azimuthing unit with the inherent advantages of the tractor.

The equipment fitted to both types of tractor is much the same. All towing gear is installed very close to the stern and in vessels of any size will include a towing winch. The massive fairlead is universal on most modern designs. Extensive fendering is fitted around the stern areas. Unlike other tugs, tractors always push using the stern and thus require less additional protection at the bow or sides.

A factor governing the use of tractors may well be their draft. Although the overall draft may be no more than a deep screw tug, the position of the propulsion units protruding from the hull bottom plating makes them particularly vulnerable. In spite of nozzle or guard plates, the propellers of both types can be subject to damage if the tug is grounded. An objection raised by some owners is the additional complexity and cost of supporting this type of vessel during dry docking or hauling out onto a slipway.

In Europe the use of tractors has extended to coastal towing and work offshore. Powerful Voith Schneider tractors, fully equipped with towing winches and navigational equipment,

Tirrick was built in 1983 to handle the very largest tankers calling at the Sullom Voe oil terminal in the Shetland Islands. She is one of the most powerful Voith Schneider tractors in Britain, with main engines producing a total of 4,600 bhp. A vessel of 420 tons gross, she produces a bollard pull of 43.5 tons. Tirrick and her sister ship Shalder are functional vessels designed to operate in an extremely exposed location. (Shetland Towing Company)

suitable for a wide range of operations were first put into service by the Nieuwe Rotterdam Sleepdienst, now a part of the Smit-Tak group. Such vessels are now widely used at sea, particularly when awkward positioning operations are carried out, with barges or floating structures.

The stern-drive tug

A high proportion of new tugs entering service with ship-handling fleets are of the azimuthing stern-drive type. As we have seen, the basic design was first conceived in the Far East but the concept has spread rapidly in the last decade or so to fleets in most parts of the world. The USA is again a notable exception, with only a few major operators using this propulsion system. The configuration of hull form and superstructure adopted for this type of vessel varies enormously. In Japan, the country of origin, tugs are very much a standard product and the design has changed little in recent years. In other Far East

Above Bugsier 4 *was one of a series of tractor tugs that brought new standards of ship handling to the port of Hamburg in the early 1970s. She was built in 1973 and is fitted with twin azimuthing propulsion units located beneath the forward hull. Her main engines produce a total of 2,170 bhp giving her a 30-tonne bollard pull and considerable agility. Vessels of this type remain the backbone of the current Hamburg tug fleet.* (L.O. Amboldt)

and Australasian fleets stern-drive tugs have become extremely functional, even futuristic in appearance. A powerful propulsion system, sturdy hull, very basic towing gear, a central sophisticated control station, and accommodation for a small crew is the basic specification for many new tugs. Britain and Europe were slower to adopt the concept and the tendency has been to incorporate the propulsion system into rather more familiar tug designs. In fact a number of existing vessels have been converted to accept the azimuthing systems.

The stern-drive ship-handling vessel is always, by its nature, a twin-screw tug. Close quarters towing is invariably carried out using towing gear or a winch located on the foredeck and towing astern. Operating in this way the tug is remarkably agile and can reposition, or move in to push with its fendered bow, very quickly. The risk of girting is virtually nil. The bollard pull ahead or astern is almost identical in most vessels. Coastal work or operations requiring a much longer towline are carried out from the stern, much the same as with a conventional screw tug. There is little difference in the type of engines or power output available in the stern-drive designs. Much the same performance, in terms of bollard pull, is achieved compared with a conventional screw tug but with the advantage of much improved handling.

Ship-handling operations

Before attempting to show how the various types of modern tug are used, a few words on the basic purpose of the ship-handling tug may be useful. Tugs are employed to assist ships that, due to their size or design, are not capable of manoeuvring safely under their own power in the confined waters they may have to visit at either end of a voyage. The circumstances can vary from the use of a single unsophisticated har-

Above Flying Spindrift *was built in 1986 for* Clyde Shipping (Tugs) Ltd *of Greenock. She is a stern-drive tug of 260 tons gross with main engines of 3,100 bhp (total). Her twin Aquamaster azimuthing propulsion units give her a bollard pull of 40 tonnes. A special feature of* Flying Spindrift *is her wheelhouse, which was designed using ergonomic principles to reduce the workload on the master and crew.* (Clyde Shipping)

Opposite *The German tug* Arion *is operated by the Bremerhaven company Hapag-Lloyd. She is a Voith Schneider tractor tug used for a variety of duties, at sea and in port. Built in 1977, she is a vessel of 253 tonnes gross and 2,170 bhp with a bollard pull of 27 tons.* Arion *is seen here with a barge delivering coal-handling equipment to power stations in Britain.* (Author)

bour tug assisting a medium-sized ship to its berth in a small port to a complicated operation involving several powerful tugs working with a modern tanker of several hundred thousand tons.

The need for tugs

The need for tug assistance is determined by a multitude of factors. The size of the ship in relation to the area it is to enter, the need to negotiate locks, pass through bridges, or perform other complex manoeuvres to berth or unberth are all common reasons for employing some form of tug assistance. Difficult tidal conditions or high winds can impose severe limits on the handling of a ship in a confined waterway. Many small or medium-sized ships require assistance only when weather conditions are very poor. For example, large modern car and passenger ferries are well-equipped ships designed to handle well in all but the very worst weather conditions, but such vessels have very large superstructures that make them extremely susceptible to the effects of the wind in very bad conditions. A high wind, directly on her beam, may prevent any similar ship berthing or leaving safely without the assistance of a tug.

Larger ships have additional problems, related to their sheer bulk and the enormous amount of kinetic energy inherent in their mass. A large ship, moving only very slowly, has sufficient stored energy to do a vast amount of damage should it collide with another object or even make contact with a jetty too heavily. It is the duty of the attendant tugs to take charge of such ships, slow them down, move them onto their berths, and stop any forward or sideways movement at exactly the right moment to prevent damage. The ship may need to be turned ('swung' in towage terms) in order to present the correct side to the berth for loading or discharge. Dock systems are often entered through locks and once inside can be congested, with narrow passages between the various basins. Tugs may be required to carry out these operations in a variety of tidal conditions, which alone can pose serious problems for large unwieldy vessels.

Whether or not a ship requires the assistance of tugs is often an automatic decision. Many ports have by-laws which lay down strict rules governing pilotage and towage. These rules generally place limits on the size and type of ship that can navigate in the area without tugs. Rules laid down by the ship's owners, insurance underwriters, or wharf operators can also demand the assistance of tugs for certain vessels and circumstances. These rules frequently give precise instructions on the number, type, and power of the tugs to be used. When a very large ship enters port, decisions regarding her movements, pilotage, and towage are made well in advance, leaving little to chance.

The role of the pilot

The role of the pilot is an important one. Pilotage arrangements differ from country to country, but in all cases the pilot is an individual with specific local knowledge of the port, its tides, and the effects of weather on the movement of ships. In most ports the use of a pilot is mandatory for ships above a certain size. Throughout Britain and Europe pilots are supplied either by the port authority or by a pilotage organization and join ships entering or leaving the area to advise the ship's master on the safe navigation of his vessel. Similar systems operate in many parts of the world. In the USA the pilot may well be a senior tug master, from one of the tugs assisting the ship, put on board to take charge of the operation. During the ship-handling operation the pilot is in charge of any tugs used and communicates his orders directly to the tug masters by VHF radio. The use of whistle signals between tug and ship has been superseded by radio in most ports, except in emergencies.

The ocean liner Queen Elizabeth 2 *is seen docking at Southampton with the assistance of tugs. The tractor tug* Flying Kestrel *is guiding the bow of the ship towards her berth. The single-screw* Victoria *is close alongside waiting to push the ship into position. A further tractor is out of sight, connected at the ship's stern and towing to starboard.* (Author)

Basic ship-handling manoeuvres

A tug master will say that every task is different: differing weather and tidal conditions, different ships—each with their own characteristics—and perhaps different pilots. All of the foregoing factors play a part in towage operations in almost any port in the world.

The next few paragraphs are not intended as definitive examples but simply illustrate some of the very basic manoeuvres that tugs are regularly expected to perform whilst ship-handling. They also give some indication of how these

135

Picking up a tow underway requires great skill and concentration by the tug master and crew. The close proximity of tug and tow can be seen in this picture of a single-screw tug making a towing connection with a medium-sized cargo vessel. The towline is in the process of being hauled aboard the ship.
(Author)

operations vary with the type of tug. The descriptions do not take into account the possible effects of wind and tide, which can transform the simplest operation into a virtual nightmare. It is also worth considering that these operations are carried out daily by tug crews, working not only in fine daylight conditions but also at night and throughout the winter months. The work has to continue in the dark, with the tug rolling and with decks and ropes covered with ice or snow. Even in the best equipped tug, personnel are still required to work on deck to handle the towline and make the initial connection between ship and tug.

Picking up the tow

One of the most interesting operations to watch, and one requiring a great deal of skill from both tug master and crew, is 'picking up a tow' whilst the ship is underway. When a ship enters port, or approaches a berth, it will often try to maintain sufficient speed to enable it to steer effectively until the tugs have their towlines connected. The tugs may have to approach the vessel and connect towlines with the ship moving as fast as 5-6 knots. This can be a hazardous operation, particularly for the tug selected to take charge of the ship's bow—the 'head' tug. The flow of water around the hull of a large moving ship produces a phenomenon known as 'interaction'. A situation can arise in which the tug passes into a low pressure area adjacent to the ship's bow, causing loss of control. This can result in a collision or in the tug being run down by the ship.

In order for a towline to be passed the tug will manoeuvre within a very few metres of the ship's bow. A conventional screw tug is the most vulnerable during this operation. Tractors or stern-drive tugs are able to control the thrust from their propulsion units to combat any risk of collision. Some stern-drive vessels are able to manoeuvre astern at speed and use this method to position the bow of the tug in readiness to connect a towline from the forward winch.

Once the tug is in position, a heaving line is thrown down from the ship to the waiting tug crew. The heaving line is tied to the end of a light 'messenger' rope, which is used to haul the towline aboard the ship. In some ports a rope from the ship may be used, but with the special nature of modern towropes and the use of towing winches it is now more common for the tug's ropes to be used. With the towline secured, the tug can move into a towing position. For tugs at the stern or alongside the ship, picking up the tow is slightly easier.

When American towing methods are used the tugs move in alongside the ship and connect with short towropes from the bow of each tug. Tugs that are to remain alongside for the whole operation, parallel to the ship, may also be secured by a rope aft.

Slowing the ship down

Prior to positioning the ship for berthing it will be slowed down and stopped in the correct position. Using European methods, the stern tug will be positioned to tow astern and slow the ship, leaving the head tug to control the ship's direc-

Tractor tug Sir Bevois *is acting as stern tug during the operation to berth the* Queen Elizabeth 2. *She will help control the stern of the ship by towing or pushing as the pilot instructs.* Sir Bevois *was built for Red Funnel Tugs Ltd of Southampton in 1985. She is a vessel of 250 gross tons and 2,720 bhp equipped with twin Schottle azimuthing propulsion units. This arrangement produces a bollard pull of 35 tonnes. (Author)*

A pair of conventional European screw tugs swinging a ship and manoeuvring her onto a riverside berth. The arrow indicates the direction of the tide, whilst the numerical sequence shows stages of the operation.

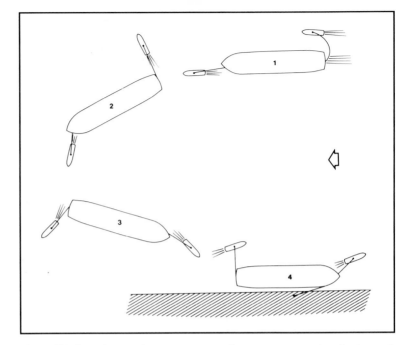

tion. Under these circumstances the tug or tractor is towed along, stern first by the ship, applying power when necessary and acting rather like a rudder. A stern-drive tug will operate in much the same manner but be connected from its bows and apply power by going astern. Alternatively, the pilot will rely on the ship's own power to stop the ship and use the tugs to assist in steering.

American tugs apply power astern, selectively, at the pilot's instruction to keep the ship on course. If required, a selected tug can reposition easily and move ahead if required.

To 'swing' a ship

To 'swing', or turn, a ship is a basic manoeuvre used to turn the vessel, through 180 degrees, into a tide prior to berthing or to ensure that the correct side of the ship is in contact with the berth for loading or unloading purposes. A partial 'swing' may be used to turn a ship into a lock or dock entrance. If the ship is to be turned to starboard, using European practice, the head tug will move round to tow at 90 degrees to the ship's starboard side. A stern tug will position herself similarly to port and the ship will be turned bodily under the direction of the pilot. If other tugs are involved with berthing the ship they may be called in to push on bow or stern to assist or control the swing. In some cases more than one head tug will be used. If tractor tugs are used, repositioning to tow to port or starboard is a simple matter and can be achieved safely keeping control of the towline. Again, the stern-drive tug will perform

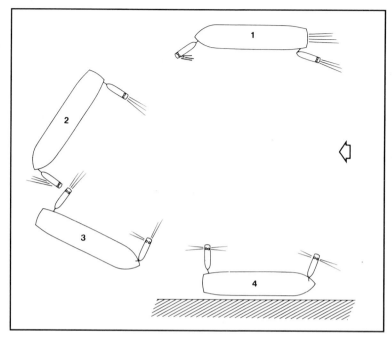

The same swinging and berthing operation with stern-drive tugs, with azimuthing propulsion units, is commonly carried out with the tugs connected by a towline from the bow. The arrow again indicates the direction of the tide and the direction of thrust from the tugs' propulsion units is also shown.

The Japanese-built stern-drive tug Kenley is towing a large car carrier from her bow winch. When the ship is in position adjacent to the berth the tug will adjust the length of her towline and move round to push on the ship's side. In this way she can push or tow at will, without disconnecting the towline. Kenley is a 3,200 bhp vessel with a bollard pull of 45 tonnes, operated in the River Medway in the fleet of J.P.Knight Ltd. (Author)

in much the same way—towing astern or pushing on the ship's bow or stern.

If the ship is to be turned into a lock or entrance, the head tug is responsible for aligning the ship's bow with the opening. The stern tug then has the task of holding the stern in line, working to counteract any crosswind or tidal flow. Any additional tugs may be deployed along the ship's side to push or guide the vessel, reducing the contact with the lock walls.

American tugs undertaking a 'swinging' operation will tow astern to port or starboard as appropriate or push on the ship's bow and stern. If tugs are positioned on either side of the ship, secured bow and stern, one will put her engines ahead and the other astern—creating a powerful turning moment. Moving the ship into an entrance is done in much the same way by pushing or backing away on the short tow ropes.

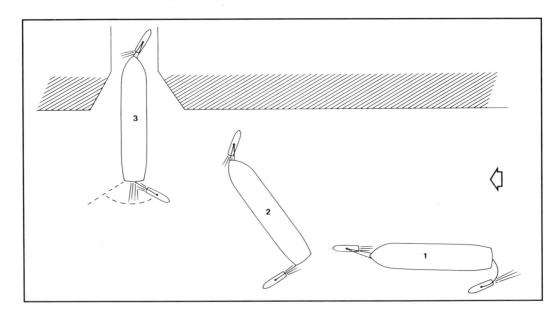

Berthing a ship alongside

Any manoeuvres carried out with a ship prior to her arrival at a wharf or jetty are usually designed to end with the vessel positioned conveniently near the berth. Often this results in the ship positioned parallel to the berth but some distance away. In European practice head and stern tugs will tow towards the berth, moving the ship sideways. By co-ordinating the work of the tugs at each end the pilot can also ensure that the ship is correctly positioned longitudinally. Additional tugs may be employed to push on the vessel's side. Once the ship is close enough for mooring ropes to be passed, one or other of the tugs may be released, leaving the other to hold the ship in position against any tide or wind. The free tug may then be used to push on the ship's side to relieve the pressure on mooring lines until all the ropes are secure.

The use of tractors or stern-drive tugs in the foregoing operation simplifies matters considerably. A tractor will tow the ship into position in much the same way, but once the first mooring lines are passed she can adjust the length of her towline and move in quickly to push with her stern, without the need to disconnect. Stern-drive tugs, working from a bow winch, operate in the same fashion.

American tugs carrying out the same operation remain connected by the bow and move round to push at 90 degrees to the ship. If some adjustment is required to the longitudinal position one or more tugs will move parallel to the ship and apply power in the necessary direction.

It should be mentioned that although the practice of tugs pushing on a ship's side is an inherent part of ship-handling operations, it is undertaken with some caution. A powerful tug is capable of causing serious damage to the side plating of some ships. In a heavy swell it may be particularly difficult to keep the tug properly positioned on the ship's side. Some modern ships have marks painted along their sides indicating the correct 'pressure points' where assisting tugs may push without causing damage.

Assisting a ship away from a berth

For relatively large ships, the procedure for leaving a berth is very much the reverse of that used for berthing. Depending on the size of the ship, the weather conditions, and the need for any subsequent manoeuvres, a little less assistance may be needed. The head and stern tugs are connected as before and are positioned initially to tow the ship sideways off the berth. An additional tug may be used to push on the ship's side, holding it in position whilst the mooring ropes are released. Once the ship is ready to leave and has been moved off the berth sufficiently the head tug will impart some forward motion, towing the ship in the direction she is to head.

Tugs are preparing to 'swing' container ship Osaka Bay *shortly after leaving a berth at Southampton. The two 2,320-bhp tugs* Flying Kestrel *and* Flying Osprey *of the Alexandra Towing Company each have a bollard pull of 36 tonnes. (Author)*

The sequence of operations likely to be adopted by a pair of tugs manoeuvring a ship into a lock or dock entrance from a tidal river. The arrow indicates the tidal flow. The tugs shown are of the conventional screw type.

Generally, the head tug will remain connected until any other tugs have been released and the pilot is assured that the ship's steering and propulsion systems are working correctly.

American-style tugs will also use the reverse procedure to that of berthing. The tugs will each be connected with a rope from the bow and tow out stern first. With very large ships tugs may also move in to push on the bow and stern, on the shore side of the ship, once the mooring ropes have been released. Because American tugs operate in such close proximity to their charges they frequently sustain superficial damage. For instance, manoeuvring beneath the overhanging bow and stern areas of large ships sometimes results in damaged masts, wheelhouses, and handrails.

In high winds, even ships which do not normally need assistance from tugs may have difficulty leaving a berth without help. A ship can be held firmly against the quay by a stiff breeze. The assistance of just one tug may be all that is required to tow the vessel's bow or stern away from the berth and perhaps impart some forward movement.

Retrieving the towline

The final action, once a towing operation is completed, is to retrieve the towline safely without fouling the propellers of the ship or of the tug herself. Even when the ship is stationary there is need for caution. A conventional screw tug, operating with a towline aft, normally moves steadily away from the ship allowing the towline to stream astern. Norman pins will often be erected at the after rail to ensure that the rope does not pass over the side and become drawn into the propeller. Tugs fitted with towing winches can retrieve their ropes quite

The Voith Schneider tractor tug Hallgarth *and single-screw tug* Bargarth *are assisting a small tanker from her berth in the Welsh port of Cardiff.* Bargarth *is a 'Combi'-tug, fitted with an azimuthing thruster beneath her bow. Both tugs are owned by Cory Towage Ltd. The ship is to be pulled bodily away from the berth and moved forward to a lock entrance.* (Author)

A view of the fire-fighting tug Greengarth *towing the* Amoco Chicago *(104,887 tons) from a berth at Milford Haven. The ship has been unloaded and is displaying a massive freeboard.* Greengarth *is owned by Cory Ship Towage Ltd. She is a single-screw vessel of 291 tons gross and 2,460 bhp built in 1970. The need for a high level fire monitor to reach above deck level is apparent from this picture.* (Author)

quickly. Others may use some form of rope recovery technique, using a messenger rope and a capstan or some other means of getting the rope inboard with as little manual effort as possible. Caution is also required with tractors and stern-drive tugs, though these have the advantage of the propellers being located further away from the towing gear. The master

A view aft from the wheelhouse of the Voith Schneider tractor tug Sun Anglia *as she unberths a medium-sized tanker. The ship is in the process of being towed stern first to be 'swung' prior to leaving port. Note the propeller wash around the ship indicating that she is also using her engines. In this situation a tractor tug uses her inherent agility to stay correctly positioned throughout the operation.* (Author)

143

Antonie Junior is a single-screw harbour and coastal tug of 136 tons gross built in 1971. Her owners, Adriaan Kooren BV of Rotterdam, employ her locally and on coastal towing around Europe. A Stork diesel main engine of 1,400 bhp gives her a bollard pull of 21 tonnes. (Author)

is also able to manoeuvre easily in a manner that will reduce the danger of fouling the propulsion units.

Coastal towing

Coastal towing is a generic term often used to cover a wide range of operations. In Europe, voyages between neighbouring countries are often shorter than many coastal trips but encounter similar conditions to true deep sea towing. Coastal towing around the continents of North and South America, Africa, the USSR, and Southern Asia is quite a different matter and can involve vast distances. In the context of this chapter coastal towing covers the tasks likely to be undertaken by ship-handling tugs or vessels of similar size and type.

There are rules governing the towage of ships and other floating objects on coastal and intercontinental voyages and these have become more stringent in recent years. Such rules are laid down by the various transport ministries, classification societies, insurers, and, in some cases, coast guard authorities. Within these various rules are requirements governing the size and power of tugs, the types of towing gear used, and often recommendations governing the conduct of voyages. Many tugs employed primarily for ship-handling easily meet the conditions laid down, in terms of power, bollard pull, and equipment. Vessels operated solely to carry out coastal operations have to conform as a matter of course.

The tug and its equipment

Obviously, the size and power of the tug used for a particular towing operation is related to the nature of the vessel to be towed. As we have already seen, vessels in the smaller tug categories also make coastal voyages under certain circumstances. Tugs regularly involved in this type of work will range in power from 1,200-5,000 bhp and in size from 150-400 gross tons. Many vessels operating regularly on the coastal routes of the American continent will be in the larger and more powerful category. The majority are single- or twin-screw conventional tugs. Vessels used extensively for the work may have a raised forecastle.

When towing at sea much longer towlines are used, generally of the steel wire type. A tug equipped for regular coastal work will be fitted with a suitable towing winch to enable the length of the towline to be adjusted with a minimum of effort. Such winches are usually of the drum type and may carry steel wire towlines of 600-1,000 metres in length. Tugs without a winch require a powerful capstan or some other aid to handle the towline.

The range of most tugs of a suitable size is likely to be adequate for coastal towing operations but is heavily dependent on the type of tow and the weather conditions. A full outfit of radar, communications, and some form of electronic position finding equipment is installed in most coastal vessels. Sufficient space is needed to stow enough domestic stores, food, spare ropes, and other equipment to make the vessel relatively self supporting for short periods.

The towing operation

In essence, a coastal or short sea towage operation is tackled in very much the same way as a full-scale oceangoing voyage. The basic principles are similar and many of the same considerations apply. The type of vessel to be towed may also be similar. Common tasks for the coastal tug are small and medium-sized ships that require assistance because of machinery damage. Similar unmanned vessels are frequently towed between ports for repair or to scrapyards for breaking up. Some of the vessels requiring towage behave very badly

Although principally employed as a powerful ship-handling vessel, the Vikingbank *is capable of a wide range of seagoing operations. She is shown towing one of the 15,000-ton concrete base units from Holland to the Thames river crossing at Dartford.* Vikingbank *is a sister ship to the* Maasbank *(Chapter 4), a 5,400 bhp stern-drive tug with a bollard pull of 61.5 tonnes. (Author)*

Goliath was originally a ship-handling tug employed by the Manchester Ship Canal Company. She is now engaged solely in coastal towing and work with the civil engineering industry. Built in 1956, she is a twin-screw vessel of 147 tons gross and 1,290 bhp, with a hydro-conic hull. In the picture Goliath is towing the large piling barge Ramlift. (Author)

under tow. Large barges, dredgers, construction rigs, and cranes are common subjects for towage and can present many difficulties for the tug master and crew. Ships are generally among the easier subjects for towing at sea, but even some of these can prove difficult. With many such vessels the need to be towed was not a serious consideration in the original design. Awkward tows behave in various ways: some yaw from side to side, others sheer off to one side and may even overtake the tug under certain conditions. The most dangerous and challenging for the tug master is one that behaves in an unpredictable manner.

Before leaving port a survey is carried out by a marine surveyor on behalf of the insurers, the classification society, or the relevant government agency. The specification for the tug will be checked, as well as the towing gear and the condition of the vessel to be towed. In readiness for towing some temporary preparation may be required. On a small ship, windows and openings may be boarded up, deck equipment lashed down, and the rudder firmly secured in the amidships position. The propeller shaft may be disconnected to enable the propeller to rotate freely without causing drag, or firmly secured to prevent rotation and possible damage to machinery.

The towing gear will be rigged aboard the tow in a manner designed to reduce the possibility of the connection breaking due to wear or chafing. The towline is particularly vulnerable to damage where it passes through fairleads and is secured around bitts. Short lengths of chain may be used to make the towing connection at this point. A length of large diameter nylon rope is often coupled into the towline as a 'spring', to absorb some of the shock loading occurring during towing. An additional emergency towline may be rigged and stowed on the towed vessel if required. In an unmanned tow, provision is also made for the necessary lights to be rigged and working before the vessels leave harbour.

A tug leaving harbour with a tow may need the assistance of another tug to help control the tow until open water is reached. Alternatively, if the towed vessel is small but awkward the tug may be secured alongside, to give the tug master better control. The towline will be rigged in readiness and the vessel streamed astern when there is sufficient 'sea room'. Once at sea the length of the towline may need adjustment. The length required will be determined mainly by the size of the tow and the weather conditions. The effects of towline length and other factors concerning towing at sea are explained in a later chapter on deep sea tugs and towing. In a tug with a towing winch this is a minor matter. For vessels without this facility, lengthening a towline and later shortening it to enter harbour can be a major task. The process involves the use of the capstan and gripping devices known as 'stoppers'. This is a time-consuming operation, requiring a high level of seamanship, in which the towline is paid out or hauled in in short stages.

While the tug is at sea with a tow a constant watch is kept on the condition of the towing gear. Any points on the towline where it might become chafed and damaged, through contact with tow beams or other parts of the vessel, are protected. At night the towline, and if possible the vessel in tow, will be inspected using a searchlight. The crew will work to a sea-going watch system of four hours on duty and four off, but in coastal waters the tug master is unlikely to leave the wheel-house for any length of time. Radar will be used to monitor the position of any other traffic in the vicinity of the tug or tow and radio contact will be maintained with coast guards or other shore stations. In some areas regular contact with such stations is mandatory.

The Norwegian tractor tug Haabull *was built in 1978 for A/S Haaland & Sohnn of Stavanger for ship-handling and coastal towing. She is powered by a pair of Deutz diesel engines of 2,550 bhp (total) driving Compass azimuthing propulsion units. As the picture shows,* Haabull *is fitted with a wide range of equipment, including winch, crane, and fire-fighting monitors.* (Author)

CHAPTER 7

Tugs for fire fighting, anti-pollution duties, and ice breaking

The salvage tug Ribut *is seen fighting a major fire aboard a tanker in the Arabian Gulf. A high level monitor is spraying foam across the tanker's decks and the lower ones are cooling her hull with water.* Ribut *is in the livery of the Dutch towage and salvage company Bureau Wysmuller.* (Bureau Wysmuller)

There are a large number of tugs equipped to carry out special duties in addition to their normal towage work. One of the best-known tasks is that of providing fire fighting services. A more recent application is the control and treatment of oil pollution in port areas and at sea. Both services have grown in prominence and in an increasing number of instances attract the attention of the media. Ice breaking during the winter months has for decades been a service provided in many northern ports by the local tug fleets.

Fire fighting

In the last few decades the increased traffic in ships carrying oil, petrochemicals, and dangerous liquefied gases has pro-

moted considerable development in fire protection measures in ports and at specialist loading and unloading terminals. This usually includes the provision of specially equipped fire-fighting vessels. In the vast majority of ports and terminals this duty has been taken on by the local tug fleet. Where tugs are already on station to provide ship-handling services, often on a 24-hour basis, it has made good economic sense to install comprehensive fire-fighting equipment aboard some or all of the vessels involved.

In some cases the cost of providing continuous fire-fighting protection is met by special contracts placed with the tug owners by the oil terminal operators or port authorities. Alternative arrangements may include partial financing of the special equipment installed on duty tugs.

An important factor in the operation of fire tugs is the provision of specialist fire fighting expertise. Again, the approach varies. Tug crews may receive special training from fire authorities or oil company staff. A common method of providing expertise is to take on board specially trained fire fighters when a full scale emergency occurs. This procedure is used extensively in Britain, where local Fire Brigade personnel regularly go aboard fire fighting tugs to become familiar with the equipment and to train in conjunction with the tug crews. When a fire is reported, the Fire Brigade are either taken on

The arrangement of fire-fighting monitors fitted to the Voith Schneider tractor tug Carron *is typical of many installations. Her three monitors are capable of delivering a total of some 102,150 litres of foam per minute. She has sufficient foam compound on board for 45 minutes continuous operation at that rate, before reverting to water alone.* Carron *was built for Forth Tugs Ltd, for duties at Grangemouth, in 1979. (Forth Tugs Ltd)*

149

The London tug Sun Essex *is shown during a weekly fire-fighting exercise with the local fire brigade. Her three monitors are delivering water. The masthead monitor is remotely controlled from the lower fire platform where the two manually-operated monitors are fitted.* Sun Essex *is a single-screw conventional tug built in 1977. (Author)*

board the tug immediately or ferried out to the vessel as soon as practicable.

The fire tug

Fortunately, fire fighting is very much a secondary duty—the vast majority of fire tugs have never been called upon to combat a serious fire. Therefore when vessels are built and equipped, towage requirements remain paramount. The only exceptions to this are the very few full-time fire-fighting vessels operated by port authorities. These are sometimes based on tug designs but do not normally undertake towing. There are a number of basic features the tug must possess to be suitable for use as a fire fighting vessel.

Sufficient space on board to accommodate the additional equipment is one important requirement. This is coupled in some respects to the need for adequate power to operate the fire pumps. High performance fire pumps are sometimes driven by the main engine, or from one main engine in a twin-engined vessel. If this method is used, arrangements are made to ensure that sufficient power remains available to manoeuvre the tug whilst the pumps are in operation. Alternatively, pumps driven by separate auxiliary diesel engines may be installed. Ideally these are located in the engine-room, for protection and stability reasons, but they are occasionally located in the superstructure or on deck. The power needed and size

of the fire pumps varies with the number of monitors fitted and their capacity but figures in excess of 600 bhp are not uncommon.

Manoeuvrability is also an important consideration. In the event of a fire—aboard a ship or at a shore installation— the tug must be accurately positioned to enable the fire fighters to do their work. A less obvious need is the ability to manoeuvre precisely and counteract the thrust generated by the monitors. Very powerful monitors produce considerable thrust, and can make controlling the vessel's position extremely difficult. For this reason highly manoeuvrable tractor tugs and stern-drive vessels make ideal fire tugs. During a fire-fighting operation there may be circumstances when the jets of water or foam from the monitors can only be directed by manoeuvring the entire vessel. If the monitors have no remote controls, once they have been adjusted it may be too hot for the crew to remain on deck to control them. Under these conditions it is essential that the tug handles well with the fire monitors in operation.

Fire fighting equipment

Monitors have already been mentioned a number of times, including a brief description in Chapter 4. In the modern fire tug the monitors are invariably of a type capable of delivering both water or foam. The figures used to describe the output of monitors varies widely and include litres per minute, gallons per minute, cubic metres per minute, or even tons per hour. Litres per minute will be used here to give some indication of output. The output capacities required vary with the type of tug and the work that she does. A typical oil refinery tug will have monitors capable of delivering something like 6,000 litres of water or 22,000 litres of foam per minute each. Larger tugs working extensively in offshore oil fields are often equipped with fire monitors capable of delivering over 60,000 litres of foam per minute. Both types of tug are likely to have four or more monitors.

The mountings on which the monitors are located often give fire tugs their distinctive appearance. Tugs working with tankers will almost certainly have at least one monitor mounted very high above the waterline, in order to be able to play water or foam over the ship's decks. With a very large tanker in ballast the main deck may be over 18 metres above the waterline. It is not unusual, therefore, to have one monitor fitted at the tug's masthead 21 metres above the water. There are a number of problems associated with having a relatively heavy fire monitor so high above the tug's deck. Apart from any influence on stability, the effects of vibration and the forces imposed on the mast are considerable. The alternatives are to build fairly substantial platforms or use a form of

A typical remotely operated fire monitor capable of delivering 3,000 litres of water per minute or a considerably larger quantity of foam. The controls can be operated by hand or remotely by a hydraulic mechanism. (Author)

mounting which can be raised and lowered. Both concepts are used. High towers of tubular construction are easily fabricated and can be both light and strong. They can also present problems of wind resistance and often ruin the appearance of the vessel.

There are two basic methods of providing a variable height monitor mounting. The simplest and least obtrusive is the telescopic mast. A telescopic mechanism is usually incorporated inside a normal mast or a similar structure in order to house the tubular extending sections. Such masts can accommodate only one monitor and this may be of limited capacity. A second method is to install a hydraulically-operated platform, similar to those used on land-based fire fighting vehicles or for overhead maintenance. When not in use the platform folds down into a convenient stowage position. Platforms for this type are capable of carrying more weight than the telescopic kind and can be manned if required.

Each monitor has a means of controlling the elevation and direction of the nozzle. The monitors may be controlled manually, although it is now common for the entire outfit to be remotely controlled either from the wheelhouse or from a special control cabin. The remote controls are operated by hydraulic or electrical systems, or by turbine driven mech-

The Scottish fire tug Duchray is stationed at the Hound Point oil terminal in the Firth of Forth. Her top monitor is mounted over 21 metres above the waterline on a permanent tower. This monitor can deliver 61,290 litres of foam per minute and the two lower ones 22,700 litres per minute. A shielded steel control position is located on the lower monitor platform between the legs of the tower. Duchray is a single-screw tug of 2,640 bhp built in 1976. (Author)

anisms using water pressure from the fire fighting system. The latter has the advantage of being unaffected by heat or moisture.

The use of fire fighting foam is the most common means of combating oil fires. Foam is used to blanket a fire by helping to exclude oxygen. It comprises a mixture of water, air, and a foam compound. The type of compound varies, as does the proportion of water and compound, giving some control over the density of the resulting foam. The foam compound is injected into the water supply, in carefully metered proportions, before it enters the monitor. Most monitors are capable of delivering approximately three or four times more foam than water. The foam compound is carried in a specially designated tank, within the hull of the tug. A tank capacity of up to 10 tons is not unusual.

The fire-fighting system will also be capable of delivering water. As we have seen, the monitors are normally designed to handle both water and foam. Often when a tug is called to a shipboard fire her job will be to cool down the hull plating or other parts of the vessel's structure. Vast quantities of sea water are used, in operations which may take many hours. Modern monitors are so powerful that in some vessels special spray nozzles are fitted for this work to prevent the water jets doing serious damage aboard the casualty. Connections fitted at deck level are used to enable additional hand-operated hoses to supplement the monitors if required.

Measures are also taken to protect the tug herself from the hazards of working in close proximity to fire. Reports of tugs working at major incidents mention scorched paintwork, cracked windows, and conditions too hot for men to work on deck. On some earlier tugs steel plates are provided that can be erected to protect bridge windows. In most modern vessels a dousing, or wetting, system is installed. This consists of an arrangement of spray nozzles that continually envelop the

Tractor tug No 80 of the Antwerp Port Authority is a fully-equipped firefighting vessel with three remotely-controlled high capacity monitors. The starboard monitor is shown elevated on its telescopic mast. The self-protection drenching system is operating with jets arranged on both sides. (Port of Antwerp)

153

vessel in a protective curtain of water. In order to prevent salt deposits building up on warm wheelhouse windows, the more sophisticated wetting systems use a separate fresh water supply for this part of the superstructure. Monitor controls are frequently located inside the wheelhouse, in a protected position on deck, or in a specially designed control cabin high on the superstructure.

Anti-pollution duties

There is a growing demand for vessels capable of performing duties connected with environmental protection. The implications of oil-related pollution, at sea and in port areas have been demonstrated dramatically by a number of widely publicized incidents. Again, tugs have frequently been chosen to carry out many of the necessary anti-pollution duties. Their availability and the ease with which they can be adapted to carry the necessary equipment has made them obvious candidates.

Anti-pollution duties involving tugs can be split broadly into three categories: oil dispersal, containment, and retrieval. Dispersal procedures are probably the most widely used and have been carried out extensively by tugs in a wide variety of circumstances.

Oil dispersal equipment

The methods used to deal with oil slicks have developed rapidly in recent years and new approaches to the problem continue to emerge. The extent of oil spillage can vary from a small accidental discharge, from a tanker in port, to a major incident involving thousands of tons of cargo released from a damaged vessel at sea. The type of oil discharged can also affect the treatment necessary. A light diesel fuel, which may evaporate relatively quickly, presents quite a different problem from a spill of heavy, tar-like crude oil.

In general the equipment carried on board a tug is intended to apply chemical dispersants and when necessary break up the slicks after the chemicals have done their work. Most fire-fighting tugs and many ordinary ship-handling vessels are capable of carrying several tons of chemical dispersant, in specially designated tanks. The spraying equipment used are sometimes permanent fittings, stowed in a convenient location on board, or removable gear taken ashore when not required. The more complex arrangements consist of long tubular spraying arms rigged to extend outwards, one from each side of the tug. Nozzles spaced along the arms discharge a spray of chemicals downwards onto the surface of the water. This enables the vessel to cover a wide path at each pass, as the tug manoeuvres to cover the oil. For much smaller operations, such as small spillages in harbour, hand-operated spraying equipment may be used by crew members working from the tug's deck. These operations are time consuming and require great patience from the tug crews.

The approach to breaking up oil slicks continues to change and several different methods are in use. A common method, still used in some fleets, is to tow specially designed 'breaker boards' through the oil. The boards are simple structures

An example of an elevating fire monitor platform is fitted to the tanker handling tug Vecta. *Her high capacity water/foam monitor is manually operated by fire-fighters travelling on the hydraulically-operated platform.* Vecta *is a 2,500-bhp vessel, built in 1970 for Red Funnel Tugs Ltd of Southampton. (Author)*

Jarven *is a fully equipped fire-fighting tug owned by the Swedish Red Tug fleet and stationed at oil installations at Malmo. Note her elevating monitor platform operating fully manned and the self-protection drenching system. She is a 2,100-bhp, single-screw tug, also equipped for ice-breaking. (Svenska Skum)*

The two Naval 'Girl' class tractor tugs are shown encircling a simulated oil slick with an inflatable boom. The tug Joan is paying out and inflating the boom from a reel on her foredeck. Irene is manoeuvring the boom into place, using her ability to move with great precision in any direction. (Author)

intended to cause a mixing action, agitating the surface of the oil and water. This method is particularly suitable for anti-pollution work at sea where very large areas have to be covered. Some operators rely on the action of the tug's propellers to do the work. An alternative method is to use a fire tug's monitors to direct high pressure water jets at the surface. A number of non-fire-fighting tugs are fitted with 'water only' monitors for just this purpose.

Booms and oil retrieval

When an incident resulting in an oil spillage occurs in sheltered waters, floating booms are sometimes used to contain the oil and prevent slicks being spread by the action of wind or tide. Booms generally consist of a series of flexible floats assembled to form a long continuous barrier. A flexible rubber or canvas 'skirt' is an integral part of the boom and is arranged to extend a metre or so below the floats to help prevent the passage of oil. The boom is positioned around the damaged ship or oil slick as a barrier to contain the oil. There are various designs in use including inflatable, fully portable types which are stored ashore or on board a support vessel when not in use.

In some parts of the world the use of a boom is mandatory at oil terminals. Once a tanker has berthed, a boom is put into position around the vessel before loading or unloading can commence. This is a safeguard against damaged hoses or other failures in the discharging equipment which may cause a spillage. The use of booms at sea, even in relatively calm conditions, is quite a different matter. Keeping the light booms in position and ensuring that the oil is contained is difficult, if not impossible.

Tugs or workboats are used to tow booms into position and ensure that they are properly maintained. Once an actual spill is contained by a boom it can be dealt with in two ways. The oil can be treated with a chemical dispersant or steps may be taken to retrieve it. The latter procedure can be accomplished in very calm conditions by simply pumping the oil and surface water into tanks. The resulting water/oil solution is allowed to settle and taken ashore for treatment. This very basic method of removing oil from the surface of the water has been superseded by many far more complex means. Among these are rotating mops that soak up oil and various skimming devices designed to remove only the oil, with a minimum of water content. Tugs are frequently involved in carrying out this work at oil terminals and refineries as part of their overall anti-pollution duties.

Tugs for ice breaking

The use of tugs for ice breaking is a duty far removed from those previously described but there are still several common

Hector is an ice-breaking tug employed by the Red Tug fleet in Gothenburg. She is a 3,360-bhp single-screw vessel of 302 tons gross with a bollard pull of 36 tons, built in 1975. Most of the Red Tug fleet are capable of working in ice and are used in the winter months to help keep a number of local ports open to traffic. (Roda Bolaget)

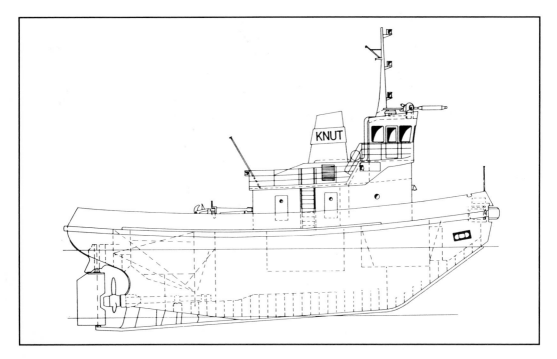

The Swedish tug Knut *has a typical ice-breaking bow and strengthened hull. Her single controllable pitch propeller has no nozzle. Note the fin above her rudder to prevent ice jamming the hinge mechanism.* Knut *is a 2,830-bhp ship-handling tug of the Gothenburg Red Tug fleet built in 1976.*

factors. There are many harbours and coastal waters which, for some weeks or months each year, can only be kept open for shipping with the use of some form of ice breaker. In many cases the expense of a purpose-built vessel dedicated to this seasonal work is not justified. The use of a suitably designed tug, to be employed principally as a ship-handling vessel, is a different matter. In North America, Northern Europe, Scandinavia, and Russia there are many such tugs. Some are employed to keep harbours, their approaches, and coastal sea lanes open as small ice breakers in their own right often dealing with ice over 300mm thick. Others are strengthened and equipped simply to enable them to continue about their normal business of assisting ships, unimpeded by ice.

A third and more recent category of ice breaking tug is the large deep sea vessel used for specialist towing duties by the oil industry. Offshore oil exploration has moved north into ice-infested areas such as Alaska. Much of the equipment used in these northern oil fields is transported by barge and towed by purpose-built ice-strengthened tugs. The same principles apply broadly to all such vessels.

The main constructional difference between an ice-breaking tug and any other lies in the strength and shape of the hull. The need for additional strength is obvious; the hull must resist not only the forces imposed by her forward motion through ice but any crushing which may take place. Additional strength is introduced by using thicker steel plating and increasing the number of supporting internal frames. The bow of the tug normally has a long, shallow, angled portion just below the waterline. In order to appreciate the purpose of this strange shape the principle of ice breaking must be understood. The tug breaks ice not by battering it with brute force but by riding up over it and using her weight to do the work. The long sloping shape aids this process and acts as a form of cutting edge. There may also be a more rounded shape in the body of the hull to minimize the risk of the tug becoming 'squeezed' or crushed. A more rounded shape will simply be forced upwards if crushing occurs.

Other considerations concern the propulsion system. Many modern ice-breaking or strengthened tugs have been fitted with conventional open propellers. Nozzles have been avoided due to the risk of ice becoming jammed between the propeller blades and nozzle structure. Small protruding fins are often located ahead of the propeller and aft of the rudder to deflect ice away from those vital components. A number of tractor tugs with azimuthing propulsion units are successfully employed in Scandinavian fleets. The propulsion equipment of these vessels appears to be unaffected by ice, presumably due to the deep immersion of their propellers.

The cooling systems for the main and auxiliary engines may also be modified. Cooling systems are often used which can be operated without circulating sea water from outside the hull. Problems resulting from frozen or blocked water intakes are thus avoided. Closed circuit cooling systems, utilizing internal water tanks and the surface plating of the hull, are used to provide the necessary dissipation of heat.

CHAPTER 8

Oceangoing and anchor-handling tugs

This aerial picture of the German tug Simson *illustrates well the traditional configuration of many oceangoing vessels. Note the after control cabin between the twin exhaust stacks.* Simson *was built in 1973 for Bugsier Reederei of Hamburg and is one of several similar vessels. She is a twin-screw tug of 8,800 bhp and 1,599 gross tons, with a bollard pull of 135 tonnes. (Bugsier Reederei)*

Tugs in this category include the largest and most impressive vessels of all—amongst them the major seagoing vessels involved in long-distance towing and salvage and anchor-handling work with the offshore oil industry. Only a decade and a half ago there were distinct differences between the larger anchor-handling tugs and the more traditional salvage tugs entering service. Economic considerations now dictate a different approach. Today's new tugs must be capable of operating successfully in a greater number of roles.

The operation of oceangoing tugs is the most volatile element of the towage business. Each modern deep sea tug represents a massive investment for her owner in terms of capital and operating costs. In order to survive in present towage markets a vessel must be capable of providing a wide range of services in a highly competitive industry.

The owners and operators of the larger types of tug are in

the main major towage companies with involvement in a number of related activities. Many have evolved from companies that entered the industry when the towage business was in its infancy. Such firms have grown and diversified in order to survive and prosper but remain identifiable by their titles. The names Bugsier, Moran, Smit, Svitzer, and Wysmuller continue to appear in the forefront of the industry among newer and in some cases equally powerful organizations. The distribution of fleets around the world has certainly changed since the Second World War. Major towage organizations based in Greece, Singapore, and Japan now secure a large share of towage work which at one time would almost certainly have gone to a European operator. Russia also has a very large fleet of deep sea tugs capable of salvage work and long-distance towing. Although originally organized to support the shipping and fishing fleets of the USSR, many modern deep sea tugs are now available to trade on the world market. Most of the navies of the world continue to operate deep sea tugs but rarely become involved in commercial towing.

Oceangoing tugs

'Oceangoing' or 'deep sea' are both terms used to describe tugs intended primarily to operate at sea and undertake long-range towing operations. They vary in size from a vessel little larger than a harbour tug, of 35 metres in length and perhaps 350 tons gross, to massive vessels of almost 100 metres long and 3,000 tons gross. Also included in this category are anchor-handling tugs, employed largely by the offshore oil industry. The anchor handler is equipped in a particular way

Wolraad Woltemade is an oceangoing salvage tug of some 2,900 gross tons and 94.5 metres in length. She was completed in 1976 with a sister ship, the John Ross, *for the South African Marine Corporation. Her two Mirrlees Blackstone main engines drive a single controllable pitch propeller with a total of 19,200 bhp. A fixed Kort nozzle of the slotted type is fitted, giving the tug a bollard pull of 200 tons and a free running speed of 20 knots.* Wolraad Woltemade *and her sister provide rescue services off the South African coast and long range towing services worldwide.* (Author)

The oceangoing tug
Solano *is one of seven similar vessels built in Japan in 1976-7 for International Transport Contractors, Holland BV. Her wheelhouse is amidships with a small additional control position located above it.* Solano *is a twin-screw vessel of 847 tons gross, and 15,000 indicated horsepower capable of a 110-tonne bollard pull.* Solano *and her sisters operate throughout the world on long-range towing operations and salvage work.* (Author)

for the work that it does. This aspect will be dealt with later. It must be recognized, however, that the current need for extremely versatile vessels, in the deep sea towing markets, has led to the more recent tugs being fitted out for long-range towing, salvage, and offshore work.

The most important feature of any oceangoing tug is her ability to operate at sea in almost all weather conditions. Obviously, the size of the tug plays some part in this. A very large tug is, in every respect, a small ship, capable of withstanding the very worst weather conditions and undertaking extremely long voyages. In almost every case the hull design incorporates a high forecastle intended to afford maximum protection in heavy seas. The hull will also incorporate some form of protection along her sides against heavy knocks when working alongside other vessels. This is usually an external steel rubbing band and perhaps some diagonal reinforcement. Bow fenders are of limited use in many of the larger tugs and can be a distinct disadvantage in heavy seas.

The superstructure in earlier designs tended to follow the traditional tug configuration, with the wheelhouse and bridge very close to the bow. This often necessitated a secondary control position further aft to give the tug master a better view astern when manoeuvring or picking up a tow. A control position of this kind often comprises a completely separate wheelhouse equipped with engine, steering, and winch controls. Another form of additional control position is the 'crow's nest', a very small wheelhouse located high above the normal superstructure. A number of oceangoing tugs are equipped in this way to afford improved all-round vision when the tug is towing, searching for a casualty, or working her way through ice.

Smit London (*illustrated*) and Smit Rotterdam *were introduced by Smit International in 1976 for long-range towage and salvage work. They are identical twin-screw vessels of 2,273 gross tons and 74.83 metres in length. The total output of their Werkspoor diesel engines is rated at 22,000 indicated horsepower. Twin controllable pitch propellers rotate in fixed Kort nozzles and a 650-bhp bow thruster is installed. The basic configuration of these vessels has been adopted by the company for several smaller vessels including two of 16,000 indicated horsepower.* (Author)

More recent vessels have a single wheelhouse located almost amidships, in a position giving a good field of view with little need for the master to change position. Duplicate controls are provided at windows facing aft with a clear view of the towing deck. The towing winches in many of the larger vessels are located within the superstructure and are frequently of the friction type. Because this arrangement is out of sight from the wheelhouse, closed circuit television is often fitted to monitor the movement of the towline passing round the various winch drums, thus avoiding a serious problem from a fouled or jammed rope.

The propulsion system fitted in the vast majority of large oceangoing tugs will be of the conventional screw type, incorporating some form of Kort nozzle. Twin-screw vessels with fixed nozzles and controllable pitch propellers are the most common in current fleets. Each propeller is driven by one or two engines. Power output will of course depend to some degree on the size of vessel and can vary from around 3,000 bhp to a massive 25,000 bhp. The latter is the rating given to a pair of new Russian tugs—currently the most powerful in the world. Bollard pull performance will also vary between approximately 40 tons and the 223 tonnes produced by those very large vessels. Free running speed is more important in oceangoing tugs than most other types. The need to reach a casualty or the next task quickly is of the essence and may determine the success or failure of an operation. Speeds of up to 18 knots can be achieved by some of the larger vessels.

The Typhoon
(illustrated) and Tempest
were built in 1976-7 for
the Dutch company
Bureau Wysmuller of
Ymuiden. The sister
ships were designed to
fulfill a wide range of
roles including towage,
salvage and anchor-
handling. They are twin-
screw tugs of 1,200 tons
gross with a length of
47.75 metres. A unique
hull shape incorporates a
bulbous bow, for
improved free running
speeds, and a bow thrust
unit. Two Werkspoor
main engines produce a
total of 9,350 bhp, giving
the tugs a bollard pull of
120 tonnes and a
maximum free running
speed of 15 knots. A
combined towing and
anchor-handling winch,
stern roller, a 'sharks
jaw', and two hydraulic
cranes are included in the
equipment installed.
(Bureau Wysmuller)

The handling characteristics of deep sea tugs have to meet rather different requirements than the smaller vessels mentioned in previous chapters. Their ability to handle well at sea, with perhaps an ungainly vessel in tow, is more important than extreme agility. Manoeuvrability remains important, however, particularly in tugs conducting salvage operations and working in the offshore oil industry. The installation of a powerful transverse bow thruster is one of the most popular aids to improved manoeuvrability. Integrated control systems are also used extensively to simplify the handling of larger tugs whilst working in close proximity to other craft. The 'single lever' integrated control system enables the vessel's rudders, propellers, and bow thruster to be operated in unison under the control of a microprocessor. The tug moves precisely, forward, astern, to port or starboard and to some extent bodily sideways, under the control of a single lever.

A comprehensive outfit of towing gear is installed. The sheer size of the winches and towlines of a very large tug surprise many people. The main steel wire tow ropes on most large deep sea tugs are between 180-230mm in circumference with a length of approximately 1,200 metres. Sufficient spare gear is carried to enable towing connections to be made using shorter lengths of wire rope, chain cable, and possibly large diameter nylon rope springs. Smaller winches are fitted to handle gog ropes and bridles and to assist in setting up towing gear or ground tackle.

Deep sea towage and salvage

A large proportion of work a modern deep sea tug is employed to do differs little from that of fifty years ago. It still includes salvage work and the long-distance towing of all manner of floating objects. More recently, work closely allied to the offshore oil industry has introduced additional tasks that will be mentioned later.

Salvage

Few tugs are now employed solely in the traditional salvage role. In the past, fully equipped tugs were stationed in strategic locations around the world waiting to intercept a message indicating that a ship was in difficulties and required assistance. The rising cost of tugs and manpower has rendered this type of operation prohibitive for most owners. The vessels engaged in this kind of salvage work are often subsidised, either by the owners themselves or by funds from government sources.

The fact remains that ships still suffer machinery breakdowns, weather damage, fires, and they still run aground. In most cases a well-equipped tug is required to carry out the necessary salvage operation efficiently. It is a very fortunate ship that will have such a tug awaiting her calls at a nearby salvage station. More often than not, a tug will be diverted from work elsewhere or dispatched from her home port. A tug being reported as 'on salvage station' frequently indicates that she has completed a towage operation and is awaiting a return tow to her home port or elsewhere.

The photograph of the disabled cargo ship General Jacinto *illustrates one of the hazards of salvage work. Damaged and holed in a collision, the ship was taken in tow and beached on the Kent coast at Bexhill, where the hull could be repaired. The tug* Anglian Lady *is seen close into the beach holding the ship in position and standing by to tow her to sea when the task is completed. At one state of the tide the tug was afloat in a hole dredged by her own propellers. At the time of the operation, in 1987,* Anglian Lady *was owned by Klyne Tugs (Lowestoft) Ltd but has since been sold to owners on the Canadian Great Lakes. (Author)*

The Abeille Flandre *is one of two powerful French oceangoing tugs maintained on station near the approaches to the English Channel, with some assistance from the French Government. Originally built in Norway in 1978 for a Swedish owner, the* Abeille Flandre *is a twin-screw tug of 1,576 gross tonnes powered by four engines. Her bollard pull is quoted as 160 tons on four engines and 100 tons when running on two engines. Two bow thrust units are fitted giving a thrust of 8 tons. The entire propulsion system can be controlled by an integrated single lever 'joystick' control system. Her present owner is Les Abeilles International of Le Havre.* (J. Carney)

There is a romantic notion that successful salvage operations produce rich rewards for owners and crews alike. This is still occasionally the case, but salvage specialists will argue that the massive costs of spectacular and difficult operations are rarely met by the resulting remuneration. This has resulted in a marked decline in the interest shown in salvage by many operators.

For many years the industry has relied very much on the 'Lloyds Standard Form of Salvage Agreement—No Cure No Pay', sometimes known as 'Lloyds Open Form' (LOF). This agreement, once made between tug and ship owners, enables salvage operations to take place immediately without complicated financial negotiations. Provided the operation is successful, a salvage award is eventually decided by an arbitration committee at Lloyds of London. If the salvage attempt fails, no payment is made. In these days of improved communications other arrangements or agreements may be possible. The use of facsimile transmission devices and secure radio transmission enables negotiations to take place and contracts to be made privately in a very short time. 'Lloyds Open Form' is still widely used in emergency situations where a ship is in danger and little time is available to make other arrangements.

The term salvage tug can be applied loosely to any vessel capable of carrying out the work in hand but it is generally accepted to be one equipped to a certain standard. A successful salvage tug will be self sufficient to a large extent. She will be large enough and have adequate power to assist casualties in a variety of different circumstances. The size of ship requiring a tow may be a vessel of almost half a million tons. Tankers or bulk cargo carriers of huge proportions have required tug assistance from time to time due to propulsion or steering system failures. Although the first tug to reach a very large casualty may not be sufficiently powerful to deal with it unaided, she may be used to prevent the ship from drifting into danger or render other assistance.

In the chapter on ship-handling, the process of 'picking up a tow' was described as one requiring a great deal of skill. When an oceangoing tug is required to carry out the same procedure at sea the hazards are multiplied. If the tug is called to a disabled ship in heavy seas, getting the tug in close enough to pass a towline in the usual manner may be impossible. In high winds a ship without power may be drifting considerably. There are a number of alternative methods of making a connection. A line may be fired over the vessel using a rocket or gun. Alternatively, a line may be floated, downwind, towards the vessel using a small buoy or float. Similar difficulties are experienced with ships aground in relatively shallow water. A tug may not be able to approach due to her own deep draft. In good conditions a boat can be used but in poor weather line guns, floats, or other methods may have to be tried.

To assist a ship aground the tug may require additional anchors and sufficient towing gear to make up 'ground tackles'. This is a method of increasing the tug's pulling capacity by using anchors and a multiple pulley system. The casualty may be damaged and require temporary repairs to her hull. For this work diving, welding, and cutting equipment will be needed and a supply of materials. Once repaired, the ship may have to be pumped out using pumps from the tug and perhaps portable units transported from shore. In more complex operations compressed air may be used to gain buoyancy and drive water from internal compartments. The need to discharge all or part of a ship's cargo before she can be refloated is a common occurrence. Electrical power may be needed to

By European standards the Chinese are relative newcomers to the deep sea towage business. The Sui Jiu 201 is a single-screw salvage tug built in Japan in 1975 for the government of the People's Republic of China. A vessel of 2,161 gross tons and 87.03 metres in length, she is powered by two main engines of 9,000 indicated horsepower (total). In the background of the picture is a Smit tug of the same vintage. (Buster Browne)

The Bizon is one of many oceangoing tugs operated by the Russian mercantile marine. She is a medium-sized vessel of 645 gross tons and 8,250 indicated horsepower with a bollard pull of 90 tons. The picture shows her passing through the English Channel with a small warship in tow. Note the black diamond 'shape' at her mast indicating that her tow exceeds 200 metres in length. (Fotoflite)

enable the ship's cranes to be used. If her engine-room is flooded, or out of action for other reasons, power will be supplied either by the tug's generators or by transferring portable units. These are common salvage tasks which may have to be carried out in remote parts of the world where little outside assistance is available.

A ship on fire can present many problems for the salvor. The fire may be fought using equipment installed aboard the tug, similar to that described in Chapter 7. But fires are not necessarily extinguished by simply dousing them with foam or water. Cargo vessels with complicated stowage arrangements may have deep-seated fires needing other methods to extinguish them, such as injecting carbon dioxide gas. Bulk cargoes of grain, coal, and other combustible materials suffer problems with spontaneous combustion. Before flooding a ship with water to extinguish a fire thought has to be given to her stability. It may be necessary to beach the vessel on a suitable shore or take other precautions to prevent her capsizing due to the weight of water used in fire fighting.

In congested waters, collision is perhaps the most common cause of shipping casualties. The damage inflicted in this way varies enormously. Flooding, due to damage below the waterline, may be contained by pumping until a safe haven can be reached or, alternatively, some form of temporary repair may be necessary. Once damage to the hull has been temporarily repaired it may be necessary to tow the vessel to port. In order to avoid causing further damage, towage operations are carefully planned. The ship may have to be towed stern first or at a particularly low speed to reduce the pressure on weakened structures and the risk of further complications.

The foregoing is intended only to give some notion of the work a salvage tug must be prepared to carry out. The subject

of salvage is an extremely wide one, on which many complete books have been written. It must also be understood that in the present economic climate salvage is just one facet of the work of carried out by the oceangoing tug.

Long-distance towing

Long-distance towing is perhaps best split into two types of operation. The first, towing ships over long distances, is a traditional one that has changed little in concept since tugs first went to sea. Again, the greatest change is in the size of ships likely to be towed. It is accepted that any ship currently in service may require towage at sea at some stage. Many oceangoing tugs now in service can deal efficiently with ships of any size. Ships are towed long distances for a number of reasons. Among the most obvious clients are modern vessels disabled by a machinery failure or being taken to another port for major attention in a shipyard. Ship repairing and reconstruction is an extremely competitive business and ships are towed many thousands of miles to have work carried out.

Redundant ships, sold for breaking up, are towed to parts of the world offering the best prices for scrap steel. The cost of towage is part of the economic equation and competition for such work is fierce. A very large tug, properly equipped, has been known to tow two, three, or even four ships at a time to shipbreakers in Taiwan from Europe, the USA, and South America.

A second type of towage operation is that concerned with other kinds of floating object. As the industry has developed, the subjects for transport by towing have become larger and stranger. In the past large pieces of floating plant, dredgers, cranes, oil drilling rigs, and similar items have been towed in the conventional way. Many of these objects can be slow, diffi-

Smit London is shown in this unique picture leaving port with four ships in tow. The ships, three container ships and one tanker, were collected from ports around the USA and towed to breakers yards in Taiwan. A number of such tows have been carried out in the late 1980s by Smit International who describe the four-ship operation as a double dual tow. (Smit International)

cult tows requiring great care, and they can be particularly vulnerable in very bad weather conditions. In the last decade or so 'dry towing' has eliminated some of those difficulties.

'Dry towing' refers to the transportation of such objects by loading them onto a very large barge. In order to allow large pieces of floating equipment to be loaded the barges are designed to be temporarily submerged. The buoyancy of the barge is controlled by pumping and ballasting systems located beneath her single flat deck. Once the barge is submerged, the object to be transported is towed into position over the deck. The barge is then raised and the object secured, usually by welding it temporarily to the deck. In this way complete oil rigs and similar pieces of equipment can be loaded and towed more safely and often much faster than would be possible if it were afloat. Dredging companies make good use of this method of transport. A whole dredging outfit—dredgers, dump barges, floating pipelines, and small dredging tugs—are often loaded on one barge. Once secured, the entire outfit can be towed to a new location, on the other side of the world if necessary.

The use of barges to accommodate large or awkward 'non-floating' items is commonplace. Pontoon barges, completely enclosed with a flat top, are normally used. Dockside cranes, sections for new bridges, huge oil refinery components, and fabricated sections of new ships are all among the items regularly transported in this way. More mundane commodities are also transported long distances by barge. Stone, coal, ore, oil, petroleum products, timber, and paper are all cargoes regularly moved by tug and barge in large quantities. The barges used in this work can vary in size up to a carrying capacity of 20,000 tons or larger.

The economics of any towage operation are governed not only by the cost of hiring suitable tugs but also by the expense of insuring both tug and tow. The premium for a major towage

Tugs Irving Miami *and* Irving Cedar *are shown towing a section of Panamax floating dry dock. The tugs have their towlines relatively short for leaving harbour but of unequal lengths to ensure that the tugs are less likely to collide whilst working at close quarters. The tugs are operated by Atlantic Towing Ltd of St John, New Brunswick, Canada.* Irving Miami *is a versatile twin-screw tug, built in 1973 and powered by General Motors main engines of 7,200 bhp (total).* Irving Cedar *is a smaller ice-strengthened vessel of similar power and age.* (M.B. Mackay)

operation is based on many factors. Specialist companies are often used to assess the risks, taking into account the type of tug, the nature of the vessel to be towed, the distance, route, and likely weather conditions. Recommendations may be made and conditions laid down regarding towing methods, the route, and the way the tow is to be conducted. The matter of insurance and relatively lower risks have been partially responsible for the success of 'dry towing'. Unfortunately for the tug owner, the 'dry towing' method has been taken one stage further and the submersible barge is being replaced in some instances by self propelled heavy lift vessels operating on the same principle.

Towing operations

The principles involved in towing over long distances are much the same as those previously described for coastal towing, only the scale of the operation differs.

Preparations for a tow are made in exactly the same manner. The vessel to be towed is surveyed and any steps necessary taken to ensure that it remains seaworthy for the duration of the voyage. Ships, oil rigs, and similar vessels may have a small 'running crew' on board to care for the towing connections, pumps, lighting, and generally monitor the condition of the vessel. Provision is made for this small crew to be housed, as comfortably as possible, in what may be somewhat austere conditions. Once the tow is at sea their only contact with the tug will be by radio.

A great deal of attention is paid to the towline and its connections. Many large barges and some ships have special fittings permanently welded to their decks to enable towing connections to be made swiftly and efficiently. These are known as 'Smit brackets' and were developed by the Dutch towing specialists Smit International, as part of a study to develop quick and efficient methods of taking large vessels in tow. The Smit bracket allows the eye end of a towline or bridle

Starmi is a Norwegian deep sea tug of some 479 gross tons, seen here towing a 20,000-ton rock barge. She was built in Holland in 1977 for Kare Misje A/B of Bergen. A twin-screw tug with Kort nozzles, she is powered by a pair of Wichman diesel engines producing a total of 6,600 bhp. Her engines are adapted to operate on heavy oil fuels and give her a bollard pull of 78 tonnes. During the late 1980s Starmi worked extensively with barges of the type shown, delivering rock from Sweden to destinations throughout Europe. (Author)

The use of a chain cable bridle is illustrated by this 1978 picture of the passenger ship Artemis K *entering port towed by the twin-screw tug* Scotsman. *Each leg of the heavy cable is secured aboard the ship and connected to the tug's towline. The ship has been towed from the Mediterranean.* Scotsman *has since been sold to Arabian owners as the* Al Battal. *She is a vessel of 393 gross tons and 4,825 bhp. (Author)*

Crewmen aboard the Dutch tug Groenland *are making the final towing connection, prior to embarking on a three-week tow with a 4,000-ton ferry. One of the ship's anchor cables is being shackled to the tug's towline. The tug's hydraulically-operated 'Norman pins' can be seen in their extended position on either side of the stern rail. (Author)*

to be secured quickly by a large sliding pin. A bridle is usually made up from lengths of chain cable, or steel wire, coupled to the towline to form a 'Y'. The two legs of the bridle are then secured aboard the vessel to be towed. The bridles used on very large barges that are in constant use are extremely heavy and designed to resist the constant wear and chafing that takes place during towing.

When taking a ship in tow the ship's own anchor cable is frequently used to make the towing connection. The anchor is generally removed from the cable and the towline connected in its place. A few metres of cable are then paid out in the normal way, making a durable and effective connection. Alternatively, the anchor can be disconnected but left in place

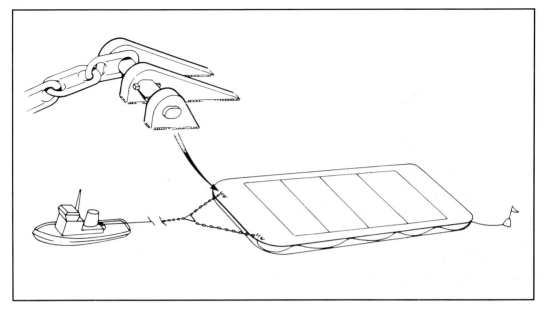

in the hawse pipe and the cable paid out through a suitable fairlead in the ship's bow.

Prior to leaving port an emergency towline will be rigged aboard the vessel to be towed. This takes the form of a length of steel wire tow rope secured at one end to bitts on board the vessel, arranged along her sides or rails and held in place by rope lashings. To the free end of this emergency towline is coupled a length of rope and a small brightly coloured buoy. Once the tug and tow are underway the buoy and its line are thrown overboard to trail astern of the convoy. If the main towline should break during bad weather, the tug can rapidly locate the buoy and, using the light line, haul the end of the emergency towline on board and make it secure. As the tug takes up a towing position the remainder of the emergency towline breaks free from its lashings and extends to its full length.

In many tows a length of large diameter nylon rope will be used to connect the main towline to the bridle or cable. This acts as a 'spring' to help cushion the towline against shock loading. On board the tug some provision may also be necessary to ensure that the towline is protected against chafing. In the more modern vessels the tug's stern is designed to avoid contact with the towing gear. Where this is not the case the towline will be protected by rubber sleeves or the contact points heavily greased.

Once an oceangoing tug and her tow are at sea the main towline will be adjusted to a length suitable for the conditions. The towline will be paid out by the winch to several hundreds of metres in length. A feature of the towline in deep sea operations is its inherent sag or catenary. The length and weight of

A common towing arrangement for many seagoing barges, ships, and other vessels. Each leg of the heavy chain bridle is secured in a 'Smit' bracket. An emergency towline is secured along the side of the barge and a small buoy streamed astern.

173

the towline act as a spring or damper, lessening the effects of snatching and shock loadings caused by the action of the waves and the relative motion of both vessels. A steel towline several hundred metres in length will sag considerably and remain deeply submerged. When the tug enters busy coastal sealanes the tow will be shortened to give the tug master better control and ensure that the towline does not foul the seabed. Alternatively, in poor weather, the towline may be lengthened further to reduce the strain on the towing connections.

When more than one vessel is to be towed a separate towline will be used for each if possible. For example, if two ships are towed, a towline will be rigged for each from separate drums on the towing winch. This enables the respective towline lengths to be adjusted so that the vessels will not collide with each other or foul the towlines. There are occasions when it is necessary to tow in tandem, with one vessel connected to another. This presents difficulties for the tug master in that he has little control of the towline between the two vessels. Its length cannot be adjusted when entering harbour or for different weather conditions.

There are also many occasions when more than one tug will be required to handle a particular tow. If two tugs are to be engaged to tow a large vessel over long distances, separate towlines will be connected directly to the vessel. The length of the towlines will be carefully adjusted and the position of each tug monitored carefully during the voyage to minimize the risk of collision and ensure that the towing loads are equally distributed. Very large tows may involve a whole fleet of tugs. One such operation is the location of permanent oil production installations. These are often constructed at sheltered coastal sites, towed to their final location offshore and lowered

The two barges shown are loaded with a complete outfit of marine construction plant, including bulldozers, cranes, a motor barge, and a small tug. Each barge is being towed on a separate towline and almost certainly from separate drums on the tug's towing winch. The sag (catenary) in the towline to the rearmost barge is more than sufficient to pass directly under the front barge without fear of fouling. (Fotoflite)

into position by flooding parts of the structure. The tugs used for such an operation are selected by size, bollard pull, and handling characteristics. Each tug is connected to a particular position on the structure and the entire operation is controlled by a 'Tow master' from a vantage point on board. The 'Tow master' co-ordinates the movement of all the tugs to achieve the correct course and speed.

A less common method, used occasionally as a temporary expedient, is towing in tandem. A towing connection is made from the winch or tow hook of one tug to the bow of the other. This method is sometimes used when additional power is required to assist another tug in difficulties or when refloating a ship aground. Provided that the first tug has a towline of suitable strength it is a simple means of adding more power without the need to make another towing connection.

Anchor-handling tugs

The duties of an anchor-handling tug are arduous and sometimes dangerous. In order to satisfy the current needs of the offshore oil industry an anchor-handling tug must be able to participate in towing, positioning, and anchoring the current range of drilling rigs, pipe-laying barges, and similar pieces of floating plant. Since the early days of offshore oil exploration the working environment has changed considerably. The industry is operating in deeper, more remote waters and in increasingly hostile climates. Consequently, the size of rigs and plant in general has also increased. The tugs required to assist in these operations have, of necessity, become larger and more powerful.

During this type of operation the tug rarely works alone.

Major offshore oil drilling and processing installations are generally built at coastal construction sites, towed to sea, and sunk in position. This massive concrete structure is being towed through a Norwegian fjord by five large ocean-going tugs of the Smit and Bugsier fleets. Also in attendance, helping to steer the structure, are one Voith Schneider tractor from Smit, two Bugsier tractors of the Schottlle type, and a local harbour tug. (Smit International)

Offshore oil exploration drilling rigs are frequently moved from one location to another, sometimes a few miles, occasionally half way round the world. The one being towed in the picture, by the anchor-handling tug Typhoon, *is the* Ocean Bounty, *a modern semi-submersible rig. Once in position the rig's anchors will be laid by attending tugs or supply vessels. When the rig is in transit the anchors are stowed on racks fitted to the vertical columns of the structure.* (Bureau Wysmuller)

She will be part of a team, with other anchor-handling tugs or oil rig supply vessels. The latter are often very powerful ships, fully equipped to tow and handle anchors. The supply vessels will stay to attend the rig, once it is in operation, to keep it supplied with fuel, water, and stores of every kind. Anchor-handling tugs remain with a rig only if further moves are to be made quite frequently. In the case of a pipe-laying barge, the tugs remain in use constantly, relaying anchors every few hours as the barge moves forward.

Most of the rigs and barges used by the offshore oil industry are moored using a system of eight anchors deployed in a star-shaped pattern. Each of these anchors must be taken out in turn to an exact position and lowered to the seabed. When the rig moves the anchors have to be 'broken out' of the seabed, raised, and carried back to the rig. The current generation of rig anchors weigh in the order of 12-14 tons, or larger in some special cases.

Special equipment

The modern anchor handler is a powerful, well-equipped, deep sea tug embodying most of the features described earlier. She will almost certainly be a twin-screw vessel with Kort nozzles and probably controllable pitch propellers. A bow thruster and an integrated control system are common features on this type of vessel, which spends much of its time working in close proximity to other craft. The size and power of an anchor handler varies but vessels of approximately 500 tons gross and 6,000 bhp are popular and economical in terms of manning. There are many larger and more powerful vessels and a growing number of oceangoing tugs are being equipped to carry out the work.

To enable her to handle the heavy and unwieldy anchors effectively the tug must have a completely clear afterdeck and a winch designed for the purpose. During the anchor-handling process the tug is often required to take the anchors on board by hauling them over her stern, along with their associated chain and other fittings. For this purpose a large, heavily constructed, horizontal roller is installed in the stern, usually at deck level. To prevent damage to the deck, a thick wooden cladding is applied to the working area. Guard rails are often fitted at either side of the working area to afford some protection to the crew and prevent fouling should an anchor break loose in heavy weather.

The winch in an anchor-handling tug has at least one drum specially designed for the work and capable of producing a static pull much higher than that required for towing. The wire rope fitted to that drum is likely to be shorter than a towing wire but must be of sufficient strength to withstand the arduous hauling operation.

In order to simplify the work of securing the anchors and their chain cables, and reduce the workload of crewmen on the exposed after deck, special handling equipment has been developed. This equipment varies but generally consists of some form of jaw or gripping device. It is located near the stern of the vessel, ahead of the stern roller, and retracts flush with the deck when not in use. One such device is the 'sharks jaw'. This comprises a hydraulically-operated jaw that rises vertically from the deck to grip the chain of a rig anchor securely once it has been hauled on board over the stern roller.

The need to handle heavy anchors, chain, buoys, and other specialist paraphernalia has made a deck crane invaluable aboard the anchor handler. A versatile hydraulic crane with useful working capacity of 10-20 tons is common. An ability to carry some cargo on the after deck has also proved an advantage when working offshore. The cargo often takes the form of

President Hubert is one of the larger types of anchor-handling tug. She was built for Union Towage and Salvage Ltd of Antwerp in 1982, a twin-screw vessel of 1,593 gross tons. Her main engines are rated at 12,000 bhp (total), giving her a bollard pull of 150 tonnes. In order to enhance her manoeuvrability, two transverse bow thrust units are fitted in her bow and one at the stern. Her after deck and winches are designed to handle the largest types of rig anchor and their associated gear. (Author)

standard international size containers. These may contain stores of some kind, or be fitted out for some special operation such as diving or surveying.

Anchor-handling operations

When the oil rig or barge arrives in the desired location, the attendant tugs or supply vessels keep it in position until the anchors are laid and known to be holding satisfactorily.

Each anchor is connected to a chain cable from the rig. Attached to the head of the anchor is a wire rope pennant, which plays an important part in the laying and retrieval process. In some anchoring systems the pennant is attached permanently to the anchor head. The free end of the pennant passes through a steel buoy. When the anchor is laid, the buoy and pennant remain attached with the end of the pennant supported on the surface by the buoy, ready to aid retrieval.

A more modern system, developed for use in much deeper water, does not use a buoy. The pennant is attached to a 'chaser'— a shaped steel collar which is free to move along the anchor cable and locate on the shank of the anchor. The pennant is used to carry the anchor out to its position but is 'chased' (towed) back to the rig for retention until it is required for the retrieval operation at a later date.

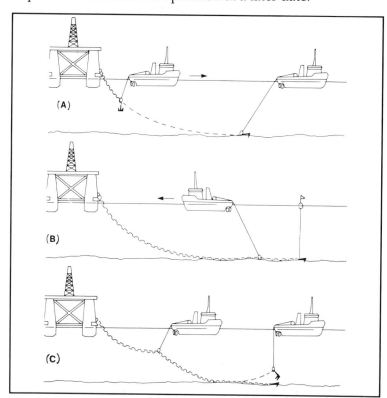

Anchor-handling operations.
(A) The tug hauls the pennant and the 'chaser' under her stern and takes the anchor out to the required position, lowers it to the seabed and tows it out to tension the chain
(B) A buoy is secured to the pennant or the 'chaser' and pennant are towed back to the rig.
(C) To retrieve the anchor the 'chaser' is towed from the rig along the chain to engage the anchor, which is then hauled from the seabed to be returned to the rig.

To lay an anchor, the tug must first take on board the free end of the pennant. The tug manoeuvres close to the anchor stowage position on the rig and the pennant end is passed down to her after deck by crane. The pennant is coupled to the anchor-handling winch wire and hauled in until the anchor is secured, hanging beneath the tug's stern roller. If a buoy is used it is taken on deck or also secured at the stern. The tug then moves away from the rig to a predetermined position as the anchor cable is paid out. Once in position, the anchor is lowered to the seabed and towed along to tension the chain cable. The pennant is then secured to its buoy or, when a chaser is used, returned to the rig. The operation is repeated until all eight anchors are in position. If the seabed is such that anchors do not hold the rig properly, two anchors may be connected to each anchor cable. This may entail the tug taking the anchors on board, along with their connecting chain, to transport them to the position where they will be laid.

To lift the anchors, in readiness for a 'rig move', much the same process will be repeated in reverse. A chaser pennant is collected from the rig and towed along the anchor cable until it is positioned on the anchor. With a buoy system the pennant is connected to the winch wire and the buoy secured or taken on board. With the pennant connected the tug hauls on the anchor to 'break it out' from the seabed. It is then raised and taken back to the rig as the cable is reeled in.

Anchor-handling operations must continue day and night, in all weathers, until the work is completed. It may take a couple of anchor-handling tugs or supply vessels anything from twelve hours to several days to lay a pattern of eight anchors in poor conditons. The crew on the after deck may be working for long hours with heavy gear, waist deep in water with the vessel rolling and pitching in an alarming manner.

Three oil rig supply vessels are attending a rig of the 'jack up' type. Once the rig is towed into position the three 'legs' are lowered to the seabed and the hull of the rig jacked clear of the water. The rig is being towed by the British Claymore *and a vessel from the Seaforth fleet. Ships of this type perform a wide range of services including the transport of almost all of the essential commodities necessary to keep the rig operational.* (Fotoflite)

179

CHAPTER 9

Pusher tugs and pushing

This final category is concerned with the strangest and most unlikely tugs of all—the vessels that spend most of their working lives pushing barges of one kind or another. This less obvious form of towage is widely used throughout the world and is in many areas a very important means of transport. The tugs fall into two quite distinct breeds. There are the true 'pushers' —known in American parlance as 'towboats'—designed to operate almost exclusively on inland waterways. They are invariably rectangular in planform and unlike any other type of tug. There are also tugs of a conventional type that spend much of their working lives pushing. Of these, many operate inland but others form part of seagoing transport systems, working with very specialized barges.

The obvious question is—why push? Elsewhere in this book tugs are described happily towing barges in the conventional way. On inland waterways, the answer is almost certainly to gain better control of very large loads. Once a pusher tug is connected astern of her train of barges the whole tow behaves in much the same way as a single vessel. To be effective, the craft are firmly secured to each other and the bow of the tug. The manner in which barges are prepared for pushing varies considerably with the waterway and geographical location. In areas where the waterways are mainly narrow rivers or canals, barges are pushed singly or in tows of two or three barges in line ahead. On wide rivers, such as those in the southern states of the USA, large towboats handle vast tows of up to thirty barges. The barges currently in use are built with square ends, to aid pushing, and are easily secured together as a single unit. In a great many areas, push-towing methods have replaced the conventional tug and barge for the transport of goods by water. The need to use the largest barges practicable, and handle several with a single tug, has made conventional towing impractical on many waterways. Push-towing on inland waterways is common throughout Europe, America, Africa, and some parts of Asia. Many of these areas have wide, sometimes shallow waterways, running for many hundreds of miles, acting as major thoroughfares for cargoes moving inland from the coastal ports. In Britain the waterways are less suited to push-towing with vessels of any size. The population of true pusher tugs is therefore very small and rather specialized. To undertake push-towing operations under these differing conditions, a wide variety of vessels of different sizes and designs are used, but all operate in a similar manner.

In pushing operations at sea, weather conditions enter the equation and introduce other complications. The seagoing tug/barge unit resembles a ship with a detachable power unit. The tug used in this type of operation is normally of the conventional screw type, suitably modified for the work. The barges used are adapted at the stern to accommodate the bow of the tug. Very sophisticated fully integrated systems are very much like a ship when assembled, with the tug fitting deep into the stern of the vessel.

The aim of all tug and barge combinations is to maximize the use of the most expensive components of the transport system—the power unit and the crew. One tug can service many barges, delivering cargoes, returning empty craft, or deploying them to other locations to load return cargoes. The tug does not have to remain idle during loading or unloading operations and, if properly organized, can remain in operation more or less continuously. A useful by-product of the barge is that it can provide a convenient means of short-term storage, particularly for bulk cargoes. Once loaded, and if necessary weather-proofed, barges can remain at convenient moorings until required, offering a high degree of security.

The German pusher tug Herkules III *is a triple-screw tug of 37 metres in length, 13.05 metres beam, and 1.7 metres draft. She is owned by Krupp Binnenschiffarht Gmbh of Duisberg and was built in 1972. Note the four-barge tow, tightly secured with several wires from the barge's quarters. The tug's two stern anchors are clearly visible. (L.O. Amboldt)*

Broodbank is the only large pusher tug in Britain but she has many features in common with her European counterparts. She is employed by the Port of London Authority to handle 1,000-ton spoil barges for the dredging department. Broodbank has two 500-bhp main engines driving twin Schottle azimuthing propulsion units. The hand winches for tightening the securing wires are visible on the boat deck and the tow hook on her after deck. (Author)

Pusher tugs

True pusher tugs come in many shapes and sizes but all have a number of common features, most noticeably an almost rectangular hull shape. Above the waterline the bow is square and generally incorporates two or more vertical 'push knees'. This is the tug's interface with her tow. The knees are often several metres high to enable good contact to be made with the barges being pushed. Barges can vary considerably in height depending on whether they are fully loaded or empty. Steps are constructed in the rear face of the knees or special ladders provided to enable crew members to gain access to the barge's decks, whatever their height.

There are various ways of attaching the barges firmly to the tug and the barges to each other. Wire ropes are generally used to make these connections. An important feature of the push-

The modern Dutch pusher tug Caesar was built in 1988 for use on the European waterways. She is a vessel of 18.98 metres in length powered by two diesel engines of 953 bhp each. In this picture her wheelhouse is raised to enable her master to see over the barges she is pushing. In this case the towing wires are tensioned by small winches onboard the barges. (L.O. Amboldt)

ing operation is the means used to tension the wires. This varies with the geographical location and with the individual operator. Small winches are fitted at strategic locations on the deck of many pusher tugs. The winches are mostly hand operated via large distinctive handwheels and are geared to produce the required tension with little effort. Similar winches are often provided on the barges for the same purpose. Tensioning devices using a screw thread, known as 'steamboat ratchets', are still widely used in pushing operations in the USA.

The height of the barges being pushed and the length of the tow present a problem common to all pushing operations. It is essential that the tug master has a good field of vision forward over his charges, bearing in mind that the front barge may be many metres away from the tug. This demands a wheelhouse mounted at a suitable height. In many areas the provision of a high wheelhouse presents no difficulty; in others it conflicts with the need to pass under low bridges or through tunnels. Various forms of retractable wheelhouse are used to combat this problem.

The propulsion system will invariably be of the conventional screw type with the number of propellers dependent on the size of the vessel and power output required. A twin-screw arrangement is most common but triple and quadruple installations are by no means rare. Multiple rudders and additional 'flanking' rudders located ahead of the propellers are frequently used to enhance the vessel's handling characteristics. Fixed Kort nozzles are often used to improve performance and in very shallow draft tugs the propellers may be recessed in tunnels beneath the hull. In some of the smaller tugs, azimuthing propulsion units are used instead of normal propellers to enhance their manoeuvrability. The power output of the engines will depend on the size of tug but can vary from 120 bhp in the smalest canal pusher to more than 6,000 bhp in a very large 'towboat'. Unlike most other tugs, inland waterways craft often have completely self-contained engine cooling systems. Instead of drawing water from outside the vessel for cooling purposes, the skin of the vessel or tubes under the hull are used to dissipate heat from the engine systems. This avoids the possibility of picking up debris and foreign matter, a common problem in shallow waters. (The greatest curse of the conventional cooling system is the discarded plastic bag, which can cause havoc once sucked into the tug's hull inlets.)

There are occasions when the pusher tug will need to anchor. Most have one or two anchors, located at the stern and controlled by a windlass in the normal way. These anchors are generally larger than those normally found on inland vessels. The anchors must be capable of holding not only the tug but also a heavy tow, should an emergency arise. A towing hook is

183

LITTLE
WILDCAT

LITTLE WILDCAT

*There are many varia-
tions of small pusher tugs
in use throughout the
world.* Little Wildcat *is
an American example
built in 1973. She is of
the type commonly used
to assemble strings of
barges in readiness for
the much larger long dis-
tance towboats. The own-
ers of this 400-bhp tug
are the Central Soya
Company, Henderson,
Kentucky. Note her very
basic accommodation and
exposed engine silencers,
gas bottles, and small
electric generator.
(L.O. Amboldt)*

often fitted at the after end of the vessel. The hook is sometimes used to tow individual craft when the tug is preparing
her barges for a journey.

The small pushers
The smallest pusher tugs are relatively simple vessels, consisting of little more than a hull, engines, and a wheelhouse. There
is often no requirement for more than rudimentary accommodation. Measuring between 5 and 15 metres in length, with
engines of 200-500 bhp, they have many uses. In most parts of
the world, where large scale push-towing is carried out, small
pusher tugs are employed to assemble strings of barges in
readiness for the larger tugs. This entails collecting barges
from loading and discharging wharves and travelling short
distances to and from the assembly point. The tugs handle
barges of up to 2,000 tons one or two at a time.

In the Midlands area of Britain cargoes of stone, coal, fertil-
izers, and animal feedstuff are transported by barge on very
narrow waterways. The motive power is provided by small
pusher tugs or small conventional tugs equipped for pushing.
Operating with barges of only 80-100 tons they require
engines of no more than 120-250 bhp. The size of barge and
their attendant tugs is limited by the dimensions of the canals
and their lock systems.

An increasingly popular vessel is known as a 'Multicat'.
This is basically a small pusher tug with an open foredeck.
Push knees are fitted at the bow in the usual way and a small
wheelhouse at the stern. Such vessels are employed mainly by
the civil engineering industry and harbour authorities. The
open foredeck is used as a working and cargo area and a small
hydraulic crane is often installed. Because of their rectangular
pontoon shape the vessels have a large reserve of buoyancy
making them ideal for load carrying and lifting. Twin engines

are fitted, producing a combined power output of some 750 bhp. The result is a powerful multi-purpose craft capable of working with construction barges and carrying out a wide range of other duties.

The larger European pusher

Several hundred pusher tugs are employed throughout Europe on the inland waterways systems. Of these many are medium-sized pusher tugs or conventional tugs fitted with push knees, serving the shorter routes and feeder services. Large well-equipped pusher tugs undertake the longer distance tows with up to six large barges of perhaps 2,000-3,000 tons each. A vessel of similar size, in use on the major rivers of America would be regarded as a medium-sized craft and employed on the shorter routes.

The configuration chosen by European owners is determined very much by the regular routes on which the vessels will be used. The size of the waterway, its locks and bridge heights are all factors to be considered. Power requirements are decided by the size of the barges and likely tidal conditions. The result is likely to be a vessel of between 15 and 40 metres in length and up to 3,500 bhp. Twin or triple screws are the most common arrangement, with Kort nozzles and multiple rudder systems. Flanking rudders are used in conjunction with the normal steering and propeller controls to achieve a high degree of manoeuvrability.

As previously mentioned, wheelhouse height can be critical and even on the larger vessels some form of variable height structure may be fitted. This may take the form of a straight-forward vertical lifting wheelhouse or one incorporating a more complex mechanism. Most are hydraulically operated and in the lowered position blend with the superstructure.

Gray Jumbo is a multi-purpose vessel capable of a wide range of duties. This example is used for general towing duties, pushing barges, carrying stores, and maintenance work on moorings. She has two main engines of 365 bhp each, driving twin propellers in Kort nozzles. Note the tensioning winches on her afterdeck and the powerful hydraulic crane, in use lifting a mooring buoy. (Felixarc Ltd)

The pusher tug Strasbourg *is a twin-screw vessel of 4,000 bhp designed to carry out the longer journeys between Holland, Belgium, and Germany. Built in 1966 and reconstructed in 1981, she is owned by the German company CGNR. She has spacious accommodation and a large fixed wheelhouse, but in the picture her masts and radar antenna are folded down.* (L.O. Amboldt)

Opposite *The Ohio Barge Lines towboat* Steel Courier *is typical of many similar craft on the major waterways of America. In this picture the tow is at least three barges wide and includes one vessel alongside the tug.* Steel Courier *is a twin-screw tug of 5,000-bhp main engines and Kort nozzles, built in 1971.* (L.O. Amboldt)

The vessel's radar antenna and masts are also capable of being raised and lowered. Two radars are often installed in the larger tugs, enabling operations to continue in poor weather.

A feature of this larger type of vessel is the high standard of accommodation provided. Many of the European inland waterways tugs are operated and manned by family concerns and become a mobile home to those on board. As a result there are often signs of domestic accoutrements and family life on board. Small boats may be carried to act as tenders and workboats in the normal manner; but in addition, it is not unusual to see a small car parked on the afterdeck with a small crane or ramps provided for loading and unloading.

The large towboat

The origin of the large American towboat can be traced back to the days of the early stern wheel paddle craft which plied the wide shallow waterways of the southern states. Few of those craft remain, except for pleasure purposes, but the successors of those steam-powered vessels are no less impressive. These modern counterparts play an important part in the transport network, moving many thousands of tons of cargo on rivers flowing through the heart of the country. Many old-established companies operate sophisticated modern towboats on the Mississippi, Missouri, Ohio, and Tennessee rivers and their tributaries.

The configuration of these giants is basically the same as their smaller European sisters. Again, the difference is in the scale of the entire operation. The towboats vary in size from the smaller types of vessel previously mentioned to very large craft of over 50 metres in length and 14 metres beam. Such a vessel may have a draft of less than 3 metres. The power required to handle the very large tows undertaken by these tugs is often in the order of 6,500 bhp. Twin, triple, and quadruple screw propulsion arrangements are common. The

most striking feature of the large towboat is the hotel-like accommodation, housed in a huge superstructure three or four decks high. The wheelhouse surmounts this massive structure, providing the master with an uninterrupted all-round view. A number of powerful searchlights are provided to illuminate the margins of the waterway when necessary and to inspect the tow.

The routes travelled can be many hundreds of miles long and the tow being pushed may contain 20,000-30,000 tons of cargo. A tow can comprise twenty or thirty barges. They may contain a variety of cargoes and some will be empty. This presents its own problems. In order to make up a balanced manageable tow, the barges will be assembled with the heavier units in the centre and lighter ones around the sides. Also to be considered is the destination of each barge; some will be

Above Crimson Glory *is one of the larger American 'towboats', capable of pushing 20-30 barges. Her owners are the Agri-Transport Corp of St Louis. She was built in 1969 and is a twin-screw vessel of 5,000 bhp and 43.9 metres in length. In spite of her size she has a draft of less than 3 metres. Note the massive accommodation, high wheelhouse, and powerful searchlights.* (L.O. Amboldt)

detached at intermediate ports and others picked up on route.

The use of large pushing towboats is not confined to the USA. Many other parts of the world have waterways equally suited to this form of transport. For instance, the Nile and several other rivers in Africa and Asia have similar systems in operation.

Double-ended tugs

A small but notable minority of tugs, employed mainly in Europe, are designed as true 'double-ended vessels', being fully equipped for pushing and towing. The more modern of the true double-ended tugs are vessels of 500-1,000 bhp and about 25 metres in length. A hull design with push knees at one end and a conventional bow at the other makes them unique. Tractor propulsion is used, generally with azimuthing propulsion units located beneath the bow. Such vessels are incredibly agile and have a wide range of uses.

When pushing, the vessel places her knees against the tow and is secured in the normal way. A tow hook or winch is fitted forward of the knees for use when towing astern. The towline emerges through an aperture between the knees and the vessel travels bow first. In most true double-ended vessels the controls in the wheelhouse and the vessel's towing and navigation lights are all designed to allow her to travel safely in both directions.

This arrangement is exceedingly versatile. One such vessel, the Dutch tug *Eerland 26*, regularly carries out coastal and short sea towage. When towing a barge at sea, she tows astern from a winch in the normal way. To enter docks or berth her barge she shortens the towline until the barge is tight against her knees. She can then manoeuvre or push the barge stern first if necessary.

Eerland 26 *is a true double-ended tug owned by G. J. Eerland of Rotterdam. She was built in 1967 in Germany. Two similar tugs are in use in Britain.* Eerland 26 *is a tractor of 1,320 bhp with twin Schottle azimuthing propulsion units. A towing winch is located just forward of her push knees.* (Author)

Pushing with conventional tugs

Large numbers of conventional screw tugs are used for push-towing on inland waterways and at sea. This form of operation offers great flexibility. The most suitable mode of operation, pushing or towing, can be chosen with little additional preparation.

Pushing with small barge tugs

Small conventional barge tugs are very popular for pushing operations in several parts of the world, particularly in Europe. This means of providing motive power for single or small numbers of barges is particularly economical when relatively short journeys are involved. The tugs used are adapted for the work, or purpose built. A high proportion are comparatively elderly. Many of the tugs employed on inland waterways have very long working lives. Operating in fresh water reduces the effects of corrosion on hulls, slowing down the rate of deterioration significantly. It is not unusual for a vessel to be updated and a new engine fitted at intervals of perhaps twenty years.

The tugs themselves are little different from those described in Chapter 5. To adapt them for push-towing a single strengthened knee is fitted to the bow. An alternative arrangement comprises a simple frame with fendering fitted, closely resembling the knees of a true pusher tug. Again, small hand winches are fitted to tension the wires securing the tug to her barges. Pushing on a single knee demands great care in securing and tensioning the wires which run diagonally from the after corners of the barge to the winches on the tug's deck. In general, the barges used are of the flat stern type or more elderly rounded barges adapted for pushing. As with the pushers mentioned previously the height of the wheelhouse is of

The little inland waterways tug Ruhr II *is typical of hundreds of similar craft working on canals and rivers throughout Europe. Her configuration is similar to a conventional screw tug with push knees added. She is owned by Schiffsgemerinschaft Rhein-Ruhr, Duisberg, and was built in 1939, a twin-screw vessel of 400 bhp. (L.O. Amboldt)*

189

prime importance. Additional flying bridges or variable height wheelhouses are fitted in the same way. The methods used to incorporate such devices on these small craft are often extremely ingenious.

This method of towing is common in the USA on the smaller rivers and canals and in coastal waters. The barges may have a shallow notch provided in the stern, in which the tug's bow is inserted in much the same manner as with the larger seagoing craft. In smaller American tugs the wires are tensioned using the traditional 'steamboat ratchets'.

Push-towing at sea

Pushing rather than towing barges on coastal and intercontinental routes continues to grow in popularity. Originally, this method of towing at sea was probably a natural extension of barge handling methods used on the North American seaboard for almost a century. In coastal and inshore waters barges have been pushed by conventional screw tugs for most of that time. More recently, purpose-built barges, with a deep notch located at the stern to accept the tug's bow, have transformed this method of towing. In fact, there is now only a very slim distinction between these tugs and their barges and the very latest fully integrated tug/barge systems.

Over the last few decades tug and barge transport has been adopted by companies in Scandinavia, Northern Europe, and in the Middle and Far East, on both coastal and deep sea routes. The method is particularly suited to bulk cargoes of various kinds, coal, ore, stone, crude oil, and petroleum products being the most common. Specially constructed carriers are in use to carry timber, forest products, cars, and cattle. The

The American tug Mary Turecamo *is shown here with her bow in the notch of a barge she is pushing. She is a twin-screw tug of 263 tons gross and 3,450 bhp built in 1973. Her high secondary wheelhouse is a permanent structure carrying the mast, radar, etc.* (L.O. Amboldt)

The tug Weswear *is operated by a British subsidiary of the famous Danish company Svitzer. She is a tug of 150 tons gross and 1,450 bhp adapted to push barges of colliery waste out to sea for dumping, from the ports of Newcastle and Sunderland. On either side of her bow is a locking mechanism which secures her to the notch of the barge but allows for the upward movement of the barge when the load is dumped. The ladder gives the crew access to the barge.* (Author)

size of these barges has also grown almost beyond recognition. Specialized carriers of 10,000 to 20,000 tons are becoming common. Some of these barges have many advanced features. Remote controls enable the tug master to lower and raise the barge's anchors, control the various lights, stop and start auxiliary engines, and in some cases operate a bow thrust unit. These remote controls may be operated via an electrical cable when the tug is pushing the barge and by a radio link when it is streamed astern on a towline.

The tugs engaged in this type of work are what may be best described as medium-sized conventional screw vessels. Most have a twin-screw propulsion system with fixed or steerable Kort nozzles and often controllable pitch propellers. In most respects they are equipped in exactly the same manner as a large ship-handling or coastal tug. As previously mentioned, many American tugs regularly perform both ship-handling and barge-towing duties. The question of visibility forward over the barge is again an important one. Tugs regularly engaged in push-towing large barges can readily be identified by a high-level control position of some kind. A popular arrangement takes the form of a secondary wheelhouse mounted high above the normal one. Access to this 'crow's nest' type of wheelhouse is via an external ladder or stairs inside the vertical column. Variable height wheelhouses, similar in design to those of inland vessels, are also used by some owners.

Suitable bow fendering is essential and often the shape of the bow is designed to match the notches of a particular series of barges. Unlike vessels involved in fully integrated tug/barge systems, most tugs are intended to retain a high degree of flexibility and the ability to operate with a wide range of barges. There have been many attempts to design

When the Finnish tug Rautaruikki *and her barge* Kalla *are fastened together they become a single rigid vessel. Two sister tugs and a number of barges are operated by Finnlines to transport a wide range of bulk cargoes, including coal, ore and timber. The barge is fitted with a bow thruster and many other ancillaries operated by systems from the tug.* (Hollming Ltd)

coupling systems for tug and barge combinations. The ideal form of coupling is one that allows the tug to be quickly and positively attached to the stern of the barge and automatically compensates for changes in draft of tug or barge. This is rarely possible except in fully integrated systems. The most usual compromise is a moderately deep notch in the stern of the barge and a wire rope tensioning system.

The towing winch is an important piece of equipment in the tug engaged in push-towing at sea. In many arrangements the winch is used to tension the securing wires between tug and barge. One of the most common methods of retaining the tug firmly in the notch of the barge uses two wires, one from each after quarter of the barge. The ends of the wires are passed through ports in the bulwarks of the tug, near the stern. Heavy, specially designed fairleads are located on the deck of the tug to guide the wires forward to the towing winch. Both ends are then shackled to a towline from the winch and tension applied, drawing the tug forward to firmly engage the barge's notch.

The tug remains connected to the stern of the barge for the duration of its intended voyage, unless the weather conditions deteriorate beyond certain predetermined criteria. It is generally the state of the sea that limits the safety of the tug/barge combination in the pushing mode. The criteria laid down varies with the particular craft involved but a wave height of aproximately 2 metres is likely to be the limit imposed on many tug/barge combinations. Once this sea state is reached the tug will disengage from the notch in the barge to prevent damage to the connecting wires or to the vessels themselves. A normal towline will have been rigged on the barge in readiness for such an eventuality and arranged to enable the tug to take up a towing position ahead of the barge with a minimum of effort or lost time.

Integrated tug/barge units

The fully integrated tug and barge unit takes the tug and barge principle, described in the preceding paragraphs, just one stage further. The tug and its associated barges are designed to operate exclusively together as a transport system in their own right. No longer is the tug a readily adaptable workhorse. In a fully integrated system it is a dedicated power unit for a certain number of barges. The assembled tug and barge is for all intents and purposes a ship. In operation, two tugs may typically service four or five specially constructed barges. At the end of each voyage the tug simply leaves one barge and collects another for the return journey. Thus the expensive 'power unit' and her crew are fully utilized.

The means of coupling such vessels to their respective barges remains controversial in some sections of the towage industry. Invariably, the tug fits much deeper into the hull of the barge than a conventional tug normally does. A variety of coupling systems are used but can be divided into two basic forms. An increasingly popular approach is that which produces a single rigid vessel. A hydraulic locking mechanism fastens the tug firmly into place, once the barge is prepared for the voyage and her draft determined. Other systems fasten the tug in position, without the use of ropes, but allow some vertical movement to take place between the two vessels. Once the tug is in position, electrical and hydraulic power supplies are connected to enable the various pieces of ancillary equipment on the barge to be operated directly from the tug's systems. With the most modern fully integrated tug and barge systems there is no provision for the tug to be disengaged at sea or for her to tow the barge astern.

Glossary of terms

Anchor-handling — The process of laying and retrieving the anchors for oil rigs and similar pieces of offshore floating plant.

Bitts — Posts or similar fittings of heavy construction used to secure ropes for mooring or towing. Often mounted in pairs. See also Bollard.

Bollard pull — The tractive effort produced by a tug when pulling against a static object (a bollard). May be expressed in tons (Imperial) or tonnes (metric).

Bollard — A single post or similar fitting used to secure ropes for mooring or towing. See also Bitts.

Bow thruster — A means of providing directional thrust at the bow of a vessel to improve its handling characteristics whilst manoeuvring.

Brake horsepower (bhp) — The actual power generated by a diesel engine under test conditions, when coupled to a dynamometer (brake).

Bridle — Two short lengths of steel wire rope or chain cable, assembled to form a 'Y', and used to make the connection between a vessel being towed and the tug's towline. The term is also used in some areas to describe a Gog rope.

Bulwark — The side plating of a vessel above deck level.

Capstan — A revolving drum used to assist in the hauling of ropes and towlines.

Chaser — An appliance used in anchor-handling to locate a buried anchor and provide a means of securing a pennant to heave it from the seabed.

Combi-tug — A conventional screw tug with a steerable thruster unit located at the bow.

Dead ship — The term used by tugmen to describe a ship that is without her own means of propulsion and steering.

Deadweight — The weight in tonnes of cargo, stores, fuel, passengers and crew carried by a ship when loaded to its maximum loadline.

Dry towing — A method of transporting vessels that are unwieldy and difficult to tow by loading them on to a specially designed barge.

Fairlead — A fitting attached to the deck or bulwarks of a vessel to act as a guide for ropes, to prevent chafing and other damage.

Fender — A pad of resilient material used to protect the tug's hull against damage from contact with other vessels and structures. Commonly manufactured from rubber, wood, rope or vehicle tyres.

Flanking rudders — Additional rudders located forward of the propeller(s).

Flying bridge — An open control position located above an enclosed wheelhouse.

Girding — A term used to describe a tug being capsized by the action of a ship or other vessel she is towing. Capsizing may occur when the towline is abeam of the tug (at 90 degrees to her centreline) and sufficient force is generated by the action of the tow to pull her over bodily. Also described as Girting.

Gob rope — See Gog rope.

Gog rope — A rope used in ship-handling work with European-style, conventional screw tugs to control the position of the main towline as a precaution against girding (capsizing). Also known as Gob rope, stop rope or bridle.

Gross tonnage — A volumetric measurement of the interior of the hull and other enclosed spaces. 100 cubic feet is equal to 1 gross ton. The formula used to measure a vessel can vary with the registration authority.

Ground tackle — An anchor and its associated tackle, used in salvage work to provide additional pulling power when refloating a vessel aground.

Handy — A term used to describe a vessel that is manoeuvrable and responds readily to her controls.

Heaving line — A light line or rope with a weighted end designed to be thrown by hand. Used when making a towing connection to haul across a messenger or towline.

Indicated horsepower (ihp) — The calculated, theoretical power output of a steam or diesel engine.

Messenger — A small-diameter rope used to haul a towline or rope of a larger size.

Molgoggers — See Norman pins.

Norman pins — Pins or rollers which can be erected at the tug's after bulwarks to guide the towline and prevent it passing over the vessel's beam. Also known as Molgoggers or Stop pins.

Nozzle (Propulsion) — A device mounted around the propeller to augment thrust.

Pendant — A short length of steel wire rope attached to the end of a fibre rope towline to resist wear and chafing.

Pitch (Propeller) — The distance the propeller will advance during one complete rotation.

Push knees — Structures fitted to the hull of a tug to enable it to push barges with a minimum risk of damage to either craft.

Rubbing band — A band of resilient material fitted around the hull of a vessel as protection against impact damage.

Ship-handling — Giving assistance to ships in confined waterways when they have insufficient manoeuvrability to proceed unaided.

Skeg — A fixed rudder-like fin, fitted beneath the after hull of a tug to provide additional directional stability. Also used on towed barges to improve their handling characteristics.

Splice — A method of joining two ropes or forming a permanent loop. Carried out by separating the strands of the rope and forming a connection by interweaving the free ends.

Spring — A section of rope forming part of a towline designed to introduce an element of elasticity, thus reducing the shock loads involved in towing. The term also describes a mooring rope intended to prevent fore and aft movement of a vessel.

Stop pins — See Norman pins.

Stop rope — See Gog rope.

Stopper — A device used to temporarily secure a towline while changes or repairs are carried out.

Superstructure — The wheelhouse, bridge, accommodation and similar structures built above deck level.

Tackle — A combination of pulley blocks and ropes or lines used to provide a mechanical advantage when hauling or lifting.

Tow beams — Protective bars or tubular structures erected on the tug's after deck to prevent the towline fouling fittings or deck equipment. Sometimes passing over the entire deck from bulwark to bulwark.

Towline — A rope used in towing to connect the tug to its tow. May be of steel wire or man-made fibre rope.

Tractor tug — A tug with its propellers or propulsion units located beneath the hull, forward of amidships, to pull rather than push the vessel along.

Wheelhouse — The main control position from which the tug master commands the vessel.

Winch — A mechanical device used to haul and control ropes during towing or lifting.

Index